TABLE OF CONTENTS

PEARSON
Prentice
Hall

2 3 4 5 6 7 8 9 10   09 08 07 06 05
ISBN 0-13-166819-6

TABLE OF CONTENTS

TABLE OF CONTENTS

Section 1
Government and the State

For much of history, and in many parts of the world, leadership was passed from one person to another on the basis of a "divine right" to rule. That is, people believed God gave certain individuals the right to rule. Study the cartoon and answer the questions that follow.

"Of course, it helped that my father was also a king."

Interpreting Political Cartoons

1. Those with the divine right were generally of royal birth. These individuals would then be succeeded by their children. Which part of the cartoon demonstrates this concept?

2. Those under royal rule believed that they must obey the king as they would obey God. How does the position of the king in this cartoon give him a God-like presence?

3. Is the cartoonist in favor of or opposed to the theory of divine right? How do you know?

4. **Making Comparisons** What do you think is the difference between a king and a dictator? Explain how the cartoon illustrates this distinction.

Section 2
Forms of Government

Dictatorship has been described as the opposite of a democracy, both in the structure of the government and in the principles upon which it is based. The cartoon below, from 1933, deals with Nazi Germany's dictator Adolf Hitler, who took power in that year. Study it and answer the questions that follow.

Reprinted with permission from the April 12, 1993 issue of The Nation

Carl Rose: 1933

Interpreting Political Cartoons

1. Describe what is happening in the cartoon.

2. Hitler had absolute authority in Nazi Germany. Does that fact explain why the cartoon blames Hitler personally for the treatment of German minorities? Explain.

3. Why might a minority group in the situation shown by the cartoon go along with a dictator's demand?

4. **Drawing Conclusions** Why do you think Hitler wanted German minorities to tell the world they were doing well?

Section 3
Basic Concepts of Democracy

The concept of democracy lies at the heart of the American way of life. One important ingredient needed to maintain a successful democracy is compromise. Sometimes referred to as "an art," compromise is not always easily achieved. Study the cartoon below and answer the questions that follow.

"We can't come to an agreement about how to fix your car, Mr. Simons. Sometimes that's the way things happen in a democracy."

Interpreting Political Cartoons

1. Describe what is happening in the cartoon.

2. Which of the five basic concepts of democracy is being ignored by the mechanics?

3. What other concept of democracy, if applied here, would have allowed the mechanics to come to a conclusion on how to fix the car?

4. **Identifying Assumptions** Does the cartoon appear to be arguing that businesses should be governed as democracies? Explain.

The development of the United States judicial system has roots at least as far back as the 1100s. It has continued to develop in recent years, with much publicized cases like the 1995 trial of football and movie star O.J. Simpson capturing the attention of the media and the world. Simpson, accused of murdering his ex-wife and another man, was tried and acquitted. Study the cartoon below and answer the questions that follow.

Interpreting Political Cartoons

1. What are the first three figures in the cartoon meant to represent?

2. What are the figures shown under 1995 supposed to represent? Why did the cartoonist select this theme?

3. **Recognizing Bias** Do you think the cartoon portrays the evolution of our judicial system fairly? Why?

CHAPTER 2 — Section 2
The Coming of Independence

In the 1760s, British taxes such as the Stamp Act enraged many American colonists, who objected to "taxation without representation." This famous phrase has survived as an expression of American hostility toward unfair laws and oppressive taxation. Study the cartoon below and answer the questions that follow.

©The New Yorker Collection 1970 J.B. Handelsman from cartoonbank.com. All Rights Reserved.

"You know, the idea of taxation with representation doesn't appeal to me very much, either."

Interpreting Political Cartoons

1. What is the setting of this cartoon?

2. What opinion is the character expressing about taxation?

3. Do you think the opinion expressed by the characters in the cartoon is representative of the time they lived in or more appropriate to current times?

4. **Recognizing Cause and Effect** If the view of the colonists shown here had been prevalent in the revolutionary era, do you think that would have affected the outcome of the Revolution and the events that followed?

The period before the drafting and signing of the Constitution was a critical period for the future of the United States of America. A group of former colonies with different resources, aspirations, and philosophies had to decide how they were going to unite to become one country with one central government. Study the cartoon below and answer the questions that follow.

Interpreting Political Cartoons

1. What historical figures are shown here?

2. What are they trying to do?

3. Why do you think they are looking at so many flags? What do you think makes their decision so difficult?

4. **Identifying Central Issues** What is the main point being made in this cartoon?

Section 4
Creating the Constitution

When the Framers met to draft the Constitution, they faced an enormously challenging task. Issues that they debated then, such as which branch of government would have the authority to declare war, still raise questions in our time. Study the cartoon below and answer the questions that follow.

William Costello/Indianapolis News

© Prentice-Hall, Inc.

Interpreting Political Cartoons

1. Who are the characters gathered around the table supposed to be?

2. What are they doing?

3. What is the significance of the captions? What does the interaction between the characters demonstrate about the Constitution?

4. **Identifying Assumptions** According to the Constitution, does the President really have the power to declare war?

The Constitution took effect not when it was signed by the Framers in Philadelphia in 1787 but when it was ratified by nine of the States. A spirited debate between Federalists and Anti-Federalists took place as the States decided whether to back the new Constitution. The cartoon below appeared shortly after New York's approval of the Constitution in 1788. Study it and answer the questions that follow.

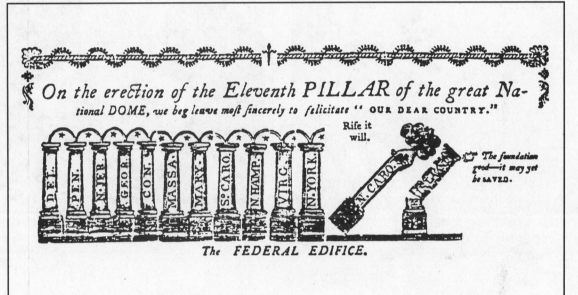

Interpreting Political Cartoons

1. What do the pillars represent? Why are some, but not all, of the pillars standing upright?

2. What is the "eleventh pillar of the great national dome" that the cartoon refers to?

3. According to the cartoon, which two States had yet to ratify the Constitution?

4. Was the creator of this cartoon a Federalist or an Anti-Federalist? Explain your answer.

5. **Identifying Central Issues** Why do you think supporters of the Constitution thought that it was important for every State to ratify the Constitution? Explain your answer.

CHAPTER 3

Section 1
The Six Basic Principles

Throughout American history, the complex relationship between the President and Congress has provided cartoonists with one of their most enduring and interesting topics. Below are two cartoons that explore this relationship. The first cartoon dates from 1915, when Woodrow Wilson was President; the second cartoon dates from 1993, when Bill Clinton was President. Study the cartoons below and answer the questions that follow.

Dick Locher ©Tribune Media Services, Inc. All Rights Reserved.
Reprinted with permission.

O.K. Berezmon/The Evening Star

© Prentice-Hall, Inc.

Interpreting Political Cartoons

1. What symbols are used in the two cartoons to describe the interaction between the President and Congress?

2. How do both cartoons express the idea that the President and Congress must trust one another?

3. How does the cartoon at the right reflect the principle of checks and balances?

4. **Recognizing Ideologies** An old saying goes, "It takes two to tango." Explain that saying in the context of the first cartoon and the United States Constitution.

The Framers of the Constitution knew they could not possibly foresee all the changes that could impact their new country, so they included mechanisms to allow future generations to adapt the Constitution to changing times. However, the amendment process they created is rigorous, and many proposed amendments do not make it into the Constitution. In the mid-1990s, the balanced budget and term limits amendments were popular proposals that never had enough support to become ratified amendments. Study the cartoon below and answer the questions that follow.

from Herblock: *A Cartoonist's Life* (Times Books, 1998)

Interpreting Political Cartoons

1. What mythical figures do the characters in the coffins represent?

2. What do the coffins represent?

3. What is the cartoonist saying about the amendments?

4. **Identifying Alternatives** What is another way that the concept of this cartoon could be illustrated?

Section 3
Constitutional Change by Other Means

The process of informal change is an effective way to keep the Constitution up to date. The Supreme Court is constantly reviewing decisions of lower courts and, in the process, continuously reinterpreting the Constitution. Since its landmark decision in 1962 outlawing organized, officially-sponsored prayers in school, the Supreme Court has continued the process of informal change to the Constitution and continued to place restrictions on school prayer. Study the cartoon below and answer the following questions.

Interpreting Political Cartoons

1. What is the coach about to do?

2. What is the "High Court"?

3. Why is the coach telling the players to pretend they are looking for a contact lens?

4. **Demonstrating Reasoned Judgment** How does the Supreme Court's ability to change the Constitution informally serve as a check and balance on the other branches of government?

Section 1 **CHAPTER 4**

Federalism: the Division of Power

In the 1990s, the Supreme Court issued several rulings that decreased the power of the Federal Government, resulting in increased power for the States. Some people think that decreased federal power leaves the most vulnerable groups in our society with less protection. Study the cartoon below and answer the following questions.

John Sherffius/St. Louis Post-Dispatch

Interpreting Political Cartoons

1. What do the three branches of the tree represent?

2. Who are the people in the black robes and the people on the far right?

3. What is the significance of the judge sawing into the branch with a saw marked "STATES RIGHTS"?

4. Do you think the cartoonist is supporting federalism or State's rights? Why?

5. **Demonstrating Reasoned Judgment** Who do you think should be responsible for the figures on the right—the Federal Government or the States? Explain.

© Prentice-Hall, Inc.

Section 2
The National Government and the 50 States

The 1996 Welfare Reform Act resulted in 50 separate State welfare systems. Primary responsibility for welfare shifted from the Federal Government to individual States. Study the cartoon below and answer the questions that follow.

Interpreting Political Cartoons

1. Who does each person in the cartoon represent?

2. Why do you think the house on the truck looks old and battered?

3. What is the attitude of the driver toward the delivery of the house? What is the attitude of the man with the briefcase?

4. **Drawing Conclusions** What do you think are some of the advantages and disadvantages of welfare programs that are controlled by each individual State?

Although States cannot act like independent countries, our Constitution does allow States to enter into agreements with one another for many purposes, such as the sharing of law enforcement information and the conservation of air, water, and wildlife. In many cases, however, States establish very different regulations from those in neighboring States. For example, California has developed more stringent air pollution controls than its surrounding States. Study the cartoon below and answer the questions that follow.

STATE LINE

"They have very strict anti-pollution laws in this state."

Interpreting Political Cartoons

1. What is happening as the car moves from one State to another?

2. Does the cartoon imply that States have little power or a lot of power over environmental resources?

3. Do you think the cartoonist would like to see more cooperation between States? Explain your answer.

4. **Predicting Consequences** What might happen if States have vastly different policies toward essential resources like air and water?

Section 1
Parties and What They Do

Although the two major American political parties—the Democrats and Republicans—are often at odds on a variety of issues, occasionally they are in agreement. This coming together is called "bipartisanship." This cartoon illustrates a bipartisan push to increase American participation in world markets. Study the cartoon below and answer the questions that follow.

Interpreting Political Cartoons

1. Who do the three figures in the cartoon represent?

2. What is the significance of their throwing this person into a pool labeled "world markets"?

3. What is the importance of the sign "sink or swim"?

4. What is the attitude of the cartoonist toward U.S. labor?

5. **Identifying Assumptions** What is the assumption about the relationship between U.S. labor and world markets? Do you think that it is valid?

In recent years, fewer voters are identifying with traditional political parties, preferring to remain independent. The views of both the Democrats and Republicans have moved closer on certain issues as a way to gain support from independent voters. As a result, some of the traditional differences between the national parties have been blurred. Study the cartoon below and answer the questions that follow.

"My God! I went to sleep a Democrat and I've awakened a Republican."

Interpreting Political Cartoons

1. Summarize the message of the cartoon in a single sentence.

2. Is the speaker in the cartoon likely to remain a loyal Republican? Why or why not?

3. Do you think it is the political parties or the voters who are more responsible for the lack of party loyalty reflected in this cartoon? Explain.

4. **Recognizing Cause and Effect** Explain how party leaders might help with the problem identified in this cartoon.

CHAPTER 5

Section 3
The Two-Party System in American History

A major issue that divides Republicans and Democrats is the economy. The Democrats are seen as the party more likely to have government intervene in economic matters, while the Republicans are seen as the party more likely to allow the economy to follow its own course without intervention. Study the cartoon below and answer the questions that follow.

Interpreting Political Cartoons

1. Irony is saying the opposite of what one means. What is the irony of the caption in this cartoon?

2. What will be the consequence of the actions of both parties?

3. What is the attitude of the cartoonist toward the economic policies of the Republicans and the Democrats?

4. **Identifying Assumptions** Explain the assumption the cartoonist holds about the state of the U.S. economy.

Section 4
The Minor Parties

In the history of American presidential politics there have been many third party candidates, but few have received more than a small percentage of the total vote. In 2000, Ralph Nader ran for President as a Green Party candidate. Four years later, he campaigned for the presidency once again, this time as an Independent. Study the cartoon below and answer the questions that follow.

Rob Chambers/The Signal

Interpreting Political Cartoons

1. What does the boxing ring represent?

2. Why are Bush and Gore standing next to one another, facing Nader?

3. What does the cartoonist think about Ralph Nader's chances against Bush and Gore? List two details that support your conclusion.

4. **Demonstrating Reasoned Judgment** This cartoon appeared a few days before Election Day. Did the results of the 2000 election support or challenge the cartoonist's view of Ralph Nader?

Section 5
Party Organization

The high costs of political campaigns has made it more difficult for candidates who are not the choice of their party's established leadership to capture their party's nomination. In the 2000 presidential primary campaign, Bill Bradley, Democrat, and John McCain, Republican, tried to challenge this pattern by running without the support of party leadership. Study the cartoon below and answer the questions that follow.

KAL/Baltimore Sun /Cartoonists & Writers Syndicate

Interpreting Political Cartoons

1. Who do the figures in the center of the ring represent?

2. Why do you think McCain and Bradley have ended up on the ropes?

3. Why are the figures in the center celebrating a victory?

4. **Drawing Conclusions** Summarize the cartoonist's attitude toward the role of established leadership of both parties.

The right to vote in this country has evolved from the privilege of the few to the right of all citizens aged eighteen or above, with few exceptions. Arbitrary reasons for not allowing people to vote, such as race or gender, have been eliminated. Yet ultimately it is still up to the States to determine how to administer elections in a lawful way. Study the cartoon below and answer the following questions.

Interpreting Political Cartoons

1. What is the meaning of the words on the side of the table?

2. Who is in line? What is the significance of the characters?

3. What point is the cartoonist trying to make?

4. **Forming an Opinion** Every State—except Maine, Utah, and Vermont—denies prisoners the right to vote. Fifteen States keep former felons from voting after they have served their sentences, with ten of them imposing a lifetime voting ban on anyone convicted of a felony. Do you think prisoners or people who have served their sentences should have the right to vote?

Section 2
Voter Qualifications

Voter qualifications, such as literacy tests, were used for many years to disqualify African Americans from voting. The ability to read or write as a requirement to vote was finally eliminated by federal civil rights laws and court actions. Study the cartoon below and answer the following questions.

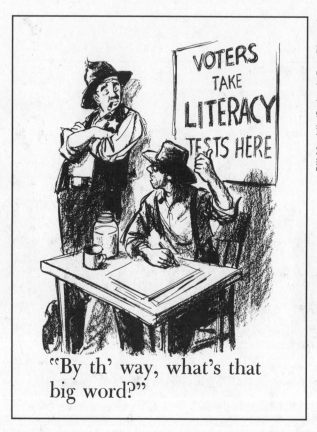

"By th' way, what's that big word?"

Bill Mauldin/St. Louis Post Dispatch

Interpreting Political Cartoons

1. What are the two people in the cartoon doing?

2. What period of history does this cartoon portray?

3. What is the irony of the caption?

4. **Demonstrating Reasoned Judgment** Literary tests were outlawed because they were used to eliminate African African voters, by giving them more difficult tests than those given to white voters. Would you favor the use of basic literacy tests if they were administered fairly?

Women first received the right to vote in this country in the territory of Wyoming in 1869. By the time the 19th Amendment was passed in 1920 granting suffrage to women throughout the country, women had come together as a political force. The cartoon below, which first appeared in *LIFE Magazine* in 1912, was the work of one of the few female cartoonists of the time. Study the cartoon below and answer the questions that follow.

Laura Foster/ *Drawn & Quartered* by Stephen Hess and Sandy Northrop

Interpreting

1. What was the _____ blished in 1912?

2. What is the s_____ g on a globe?

3. What is mean_____ falling off the globe?

4. **Drawing Conclusions** In the 1900s, there were female heads of state in Great Britain, India, and Israel, among other countries, but not in the United States. Do you think women in the United States have benefited as much from the right to vote as women in other countries?

CHAPTER 6
Section 4
Voter Behavior

Why do so many Americans choose not to vote? Some observers have blamed the voters themselves for being too lazy or apathetic to take the trouble to vote. Other observers have blamed the media for focusing its political coverage on scandals and personalities rather than issues. Still other observers blame the candidates for encouraging voter apathy. Study the cartoon below and answer the questions that follow.

©1994 John Trever, Albuquerque Journal. Reprinted by permission.

Interpreting Political Cartoons

1. Who is making the statements shown coming out of the television set?

2. What charges do the statements make against rival candidates?

3. What does the statement by the woman watching television mean?

4. Why do you think the television ads had that effect on the woman?

5. **Demonstrating Reasoned Judgment** Would you favor a law that prevented candidates from running television ads criticizing other candidates? Explain your position.

Political Cartoons

Section 1
The Nominating Process

CHAPTER
7

The process of seeking a party nomination for political office has become an expensive and time-consuming affair. When it comes to seeking the nomination for a State-wide or national office, the costs can be enormous. Study the cartoon below and answer the questions that follow.

Interpreting Political Cartoons

1. Who is the person in the cartoon meant to represent?

2. Why did the cartoonist portray the man in the cartoon in such an extreme way?

3. Why do you think the nominating process is so critical to our democratic process?

4. What is the opinion expressed by the cartoonist concerning the nominating process today?

5. **Recognizing Cause and Effect** Would you be in favor of limiting the amount of money that could be spent during political campaigns?

CHAPTER
7
Section 2
Elections

Voting in an election is an interactive medium. It allows citizens to tell their government how they feel by either re-electing a candidate or by electing someone new. Technology has made it easier for people to express their opinions on a variety of subjects almost instantaneously over the Internet. This ability to give immediate feedback is called interactivity. Study the cartoon below and answer the questions that follow.

John Sherffius/St. Louis Post-Dispatch

© Prentice-Hall, Inc.

Interpreting Political Cartoons

1. What does the box on the left look like?

2. Why does the cartoonist keep it in shadow?

3. In what way is voting an interactive medium?

4. What is the attitude of the cartoonist toward the voters?

5. **Predicting Consequences** Some experimentation has begun with having people cast their votes over the Internet. Do you think this is a good idea?

A tremendous amount of money is raised and spent in the effort to get a candidate elected. In recent years campaign finance reform has received strong support among many Americans. However, making changes in that system has proven to be a challenging task. Study the cartoon below and answer the following questions.

Interpreting Political Cartoons

1. What attitude is being expressed about campaign finance reform through the television announcer's comments?

2. What is the cartoonist saying about the average voter in this cartoon?

3. What is being implied about congressional efforts to control campaign spending?

4. **Distinguishing False from Accurate Images** Are the images of the voting public, Congress, and the media presented in this cartoon fair?

Public opinion is formed from an enormous amount of sources. Some of the more significant ones include the family, schools, opinion leaders, and the mass media. The mass media, because they are such powerful means of communication, tend to overshadow other influences. Children are especially vulnerable to the power of mass media. Study the cartoon below and answer the questions that follow.

Interpreting Political Cartoons

1. What is the common theme of the storefronts and movie theatre shown?

2. Why is the parent's speech labeled the "hardest lesson to teach our kids"?

3. What is the implied relationship between violence and the media?

4. What is the cartoonist implying about the relationship between the "toughest lobby in Washington" and the other elements of the cartoon?

5. **Demonstrating Reasoned Judgment** Would you favor a law that allowed the government to censor the amount of violence portrayed in the media? Explain your position.

Measuring Public Opinion

Public opinion is measured in a variety of ways; one of the more accurate forms is scientific polling. However, no matter how hard pollsters work to get a fair sampling of public opinion, their results cannot be perfect. One problem that occurs, for example, is that people will sometimes give the answers they think the pollster wants to hear. Study the cartoon below and answer the questions that follow.

Interpreting Political Cartoons

1. What polling challenge is illustrated by the behavior of the people inside the house?

2. What obvious elements suggest the opinion of the residents?

3. Polls can be conducted in person, by mail, or by telephone. Do you think in this case an in-person interview is the best way to take the poll? Explain.

4. **Identifying Assumptions** What is the cartoonist's attitude toward polling? How might a person who disagrees argue against that assumption?

Section 3
The Mass Media

Television is now the primary means by which Americans receive information. Television can provide more information, more quickly, and to more Americans, than any other medium. Yet this power has led many observers to warn that television is taking over the political process. Study the cartoon below and answer the questions that follow.

©1996 Los Angeles Times. Reprinted by permission.

Interpreting Political Cartoons

1. Explain what is happening in the cartoon.

2. What does the television crew member's comment suggest about the media's attitude toward voters and politics?

3. How might a television executive respond to the charge that television is coming between voters and candidates?

4. In political campaigns, most news organizations assign a reporter to report on the same candidate throughout the campaign. How do you think this affects media coverage of candidates?

5. **Making Comparisons** In your opinion, which is a more useful source of information about candidates: campaign commercials or news stories about the candidates? Explain your answer.

© Prentice-Hall, Inc.

Section 1
The Nature of Interest Groups

CHAPTER
9

Special interest groups have been seen as having more and more influence on American political life. Some people feel that the power of special interest groups exceeds the power of the average voter. Study the cartoon and answer the questions that follow.

Jim Morin/Reprinted with special permission King Features Syndicate

The Miami Herald

MORIN

Distributed by King Features Syndicate

Interpreting Political Cartoons

1. Why is the figure labeled "special interests" made to look like a giant?

2. What does the phrase "Isn't that cute?" imply about the attitude of special interest groups?

3. What role does the bag of money labeled "campaign contributions" play in the relationships portrayed in the cartoon?

4. What is the cartoonist's attitude toward special interest groups?

5. **Predicting Consequences** Do you think there is a danger to the continuing growth of special interest groups for the American political system? Explain your position.

Section 2
Types of Interest Groups

Some of the most powerful interest groups are those that represent large American corporations and industries. One example is the group of lobbyists that works for the American credit card industry. Study the cartoon below and answer the questions that follow.

Interpreting Political Cartoons

1. Who do the three figures shown in the cartoon represent?

2. What do you think the cartoonist is implying about the relationship between the two figures on the left?

3. Why do you think credit card lobbyists would want Congress to make it harder to declare bankruptcy?

4. **Distinguishing False from Accurate Images** Do you think the image of credit card lobbyists and Congress in this cartoon is a fair one? Explain.

Section 3
Interest Groups at Work

Interest groups have long played an active role in American politics. Today, while some people credit interest groups with giving ordinary Americans a chance to work for causes they support, others blame interest groups for paralyzing the government, as this cartoon of President Clinton suggests. Study the cartoon below and answer the questions that follow.

By permission of Bob Gorrell and Creators Syndicate, Inc.

Bob Gorrell, Richmond Times-Dispatch,
Copley News Service

Interpreting Political Cartoons

1. Summarize the message of the cartoon in one sentence.

2. Explain what is meant by the terms "national interest" and "special interest."

3. Why would the pile of special interest demands be larger than the pile of national interest demands?

4. What does the cartoon imply about the way in which government policy decisions are made?

5. **Identifying Assumptions** Would most members of special interest groups agree that there is a conflict between their demands and the national interest? Explain your answer.

CHAPTER 10

Section 1
The National Legislature

In the 1990s, a growing movement for term limits was resisted by Congress. At the same time, some members of Congress were criticized for appearing to support campaign finance reform while actually blocking it. Members also came under fire for hiding a congressional pay raise in another piece of legislation. Study the cartoon below and answer the questions that follow.

Interpreting Political Cartoons

1. Whom do the two figures in the cartoon represent?

2. According to the cartoonist, do congressional pay raises benefit the people or members of Congress? Does the cartoonist think blockage of campaign finance reform benefits the people or members of Congress?

3. What is the cartoonist implying about members of Congress?

4. Do you think the cartoonist is for or against term limits?

5. **Identifying Alternatives** What are some arguments against term limits that one could cite to refute this cartoon?

The House of Representatives may be viewed as the "People's House" because its representation is based upon the population of each state. However, some question whether the House of Representatives is truly viewed as the "People's House" by the "people" themselves. Study the cartoon below and answer the questions that follow.

Interpreting Political Cartoons

1. What is the contrast being made between the first and second frames of the cartoon?

2. Describe the expressions on the hiding people's faces.

3. Who elects representatives? How does this fact contribute to the irony expressed in this cartoon?

4. **Distinguishing False from Accurate Images** Do you agree with the image presented in this cartoon? Explain your answer.

Section 3
The Senate

With only two people representing each State, it would seem easy for voters to familiarize themselves with their senators. The cartoon below suggests the opposite. Study the cartoon and answer the following questions. (The television program referred to in the caption was a very popular show during the 1960s.)

Interpreting Political Cartoons

1. Why is the cartoonist comparing the knowledge of a television show to knowledge of one's representatives in Congress?

2. What is the man implying in the second frame of the cartoon?

3. Write a quote that one of the men could be saying in the last frame of the cartoon.

4. **Recognizing Cause and Effect** Who do you think is most responsible for the lack of familiarity with the people's representatives, the voters or the members of Congress? Explain your position.

Political Cartoons

Among the many bills Congress proposes are occasional attempts to place strict controls on how Congress members themselves conduct their business. The Gramm-Rudman-Hollings Act, passed in 1985, was one of their most ambitious efforts at self-regulation. This law provided for automatic spending cuts to kick in if Congress failed to reach established goals. The act was later declared unconstitutional and since then, more modest means to control spending have been sought. Study the cartoon below and answer the following questions.

Ed Gamble/Reprinted with special permission King Features Syndicate

© Prentice-Hall, Inc.

Interpreting Political Cartoons

1. Who are the men pictured in the cartoon?

2. What are they trying to do?

3. What is the cartoonist implying about government officials and the process of creating the federal budget?

4. **Identifying Central Issues** What basic principle of government was demonstrated by Congress and the Supreme Court in the making and unmaking of the Gramm-Rudman-Hollings Act?

Section 1
The Scope of Congressional Powers

The economic boom of the 1990s has resulted in a budget surplus, which has increased the options that Congress has for spending on government services. However, even though the call for government spending is great, the call for tax cuts is often even greater. Study the cartoon below and answer the questions that follow.

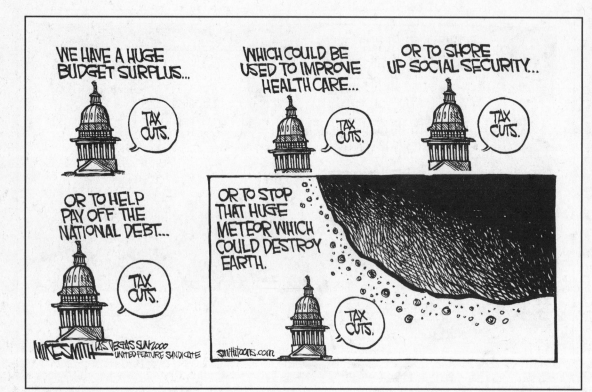

Mike Smith/Las Vegas Sun/United Media

Interpreting Political Cartoons

1. Who is proposing tax cuts?

2. On what other projects does the cartoonist propose the surplus could be spent?

3. What is the cartoonist implying in the last frame of the cartoon?

4. **Demonstrating Reasoned Judgment** Explain what you think should be the best use of a government budget surplus.

Section 2

The Expressed Powers of Money and Commerce

The Constitution grants Congress a number of specific powers. One expressed power that affects Americans every day is Congress's power to raise money through taxation. The battle over what should be taxed and how much the people should be taxed began hundreds of years ago and continues today. Study the cartoon below and answer the questions that follow.

Interpreting Political Cartoons

1. What do the two people shown in the cartoon represent?

2. What is the man on the left doing?

3. Based on the Congress member's actions in the cartoon, what does the cartoonist think Congress is doing?.

4. **Drawing Conclusions** How do you think the government can reconcile the demand for services with the demand for lower taxes?

Section 3
Other Expressed Powers

Although the President retains much of the control over the armed forces, Congress does have extensive war and defense powers. Congress's power to arm and support armies is depicted in the cartoon below. The V-22 Osprey is a military aircraft that takes off like a helicopter but cruises like an airplane. Congress consistently supported the $37 billion program to develop the aircraft for almost two decades. Study the cartoon below and answer the questions that follow.

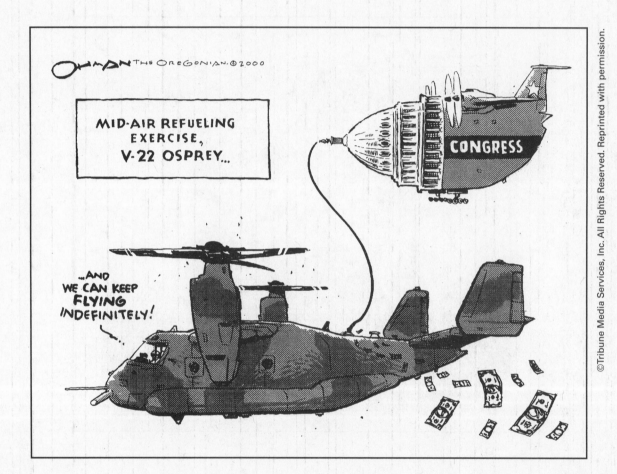

Interpreting Political Cartoons

1. Who is taking responsibility for the mid-air fueling of the Osprey?

2. What does the money flying out of the plane represent?

3. What is the implication of the line "…and we can keep flying indefinitely!"?

4. **Recognizing Bias** Do you think the cartoonist is for or against the funding of this project? How do you know?

NAME _____ CLASS _____ DATE _____

Section 4 CHAPTER 11
The Implied Powers

Congress has created and passed an enormous number of laws based on its implied powers. Some laws have endured decades, while others have long since expired. In 1978, Congress passed an independent counsel law in order to avoid the conflict of interest that might develop if the executive branch investigated its own officials. After much adverse publicity during the Clinton administration, the 21-year-old independent counsel law was not renewed when it expired in 1999. Study the cartoon below and answer the questions that follow.

Interpreting Political Cartoons

1. What object represents the independent council law?

2. What is the cartoonist's attitude toward this law? How do you know?

3. Under what clause did Congress have the right to establish the independent counsel law?

4. **Identifying Alternatives** What governmental body do you think would best investigate, or set up an investigation of, executive officers?

Political Cartoons

CHAPTER 11

Section 5
The Nonlegislative Powers

The President, as the nation's chief diplomat and commander of its armed forces, has important foreign policy powers. Yet Congress too has a role in foreign policy, including a role in treaty-making. From time to time, congressional leaders will remind the President of the need to involve Congress in foreign policy decisions. The cartoon below appeared during the Reagan administration. (President Reagan is the figure on the right.) Study the cartoon and answer the questions that follow.

Interpreting Political Cartoons

1. What is President Reagan about to do?

2. What is the message of the figure on the left? What does it mean?

3. Why do you think the figure representing President Reagan is frowning?

4. **Demonstrating Reasoned Judgment** Using what you already know about the system of checks and balances, explain why it is important that Congress be involved in foreign policy.

Section 1
Congress Organizes

CHAPTER 12

A productive Congress is dependent upon effective party leadership. In the 94th Congress of the mid 1970s, Congress struggled without success on a number of issues. In the cartoon below the figure on the left was meant to represent Speaker of the House, Carl Albert; and on the right, Majority Leader of the Senate, Mike Mansfield. Both men were Democrats, since that party controlled both houses of Congress at the time. Study the cartoon and answer the questions that follow.

"We have met the enemy . . . and he is us."

Interpreting Political Cartoons

1. What is the attitude of the cartoonist toward the congressional leadership of the 94th Congress?

2. What is the significance of the caption, "We have met the enemy…and he is us"?

3. Why are the leaders dressed as old-fashioned soldiers and carrying a banner stating "the Battling 94th"?

4. **Recognizing Cause and Effect** What is one way voters can cause changes in congressional leadership?

Hugh Haynie/Louisville Courier-Journal

Section 2
Committees in Congress

In the 1960s, an ethics committee was established in each house in order to help protect the trust of the people in Congress. In the Senate, this committee is composed of three members from each party. Their duty is to see that the members of the Senate do not violate the standards established by the committee. Study the cartoon below and answer the questions that follow.

Interpreting Political Cartoons

1. What is the attitude of the cartoonist toward the Senate Ethics Committee?

2. Identify actions that would lead to a committee investigation of a senator.

3. Do you think that the cartoonist is making an unfair criticism?

4. **Identifying Alternatives** Is there a better way to investigate lapses in ethical behavior in the Senate than through the Ethics Committee?

Political Cartoons

How a Bill Becomes a Law: The House

Americans depend upon their elected representatives to create laws that fairly reflect the interests of all the people. Only a member of Congress can introduce a bill in either house of Congress. After a bill is introduced in the House of Representatives it must win approval before going to the Senate. Study the cartoon below and answer the questions that follow.

Interpreting Political Cartoons

1. What is implied by the line "things they don't teach you in school"?

2. What is the significance of the words spoken in the second frame of the cartoon?

3. What does the cartoonist imply in the final frame of the cartoon?

4. What is the cartoonist's attitude toward the process of passing legislation?

5. **Predicting Consequences** Congressional term limits have been suggested as a way to keep the self-interest of representatives and senators under control. Defend each side of that argument.

CHAPTER 12

Section 4
The Bill in the Senate

The Senate has its own rules, many of which are quite different from those that govern the House of Representatives. While debate in the House is strictly controlled, debate in the Senate is mostly unregulated and sometimes conducted behind closed doors. Study the cartoon below and answer the questions that follow.

Interpreting Political Cartoons

1. What element of American common folklore is being utilized in this cartoon?

2. What is the significance of the news media's presence?

3. Why does the cartoonist show two senators peering out from a closed door?

4. **Demonstrating Reasoned Judgment** Would you favor a rule eliminating closed door sessions in the Senate? Explain your position.

Section 1

The President's Job Description

The President has many important roles to fulfill. The President is held responsible for the health of the economy in both good times and bad. Voters expect the President to propose legislation that will make the economy grow and provide more jobs. Shortly after George W. Bush, commonly known as "W", took office in 2001, the economy stopped growing and unemployment rose. Study the cartoon below and answer the questions that follow.

Ken Davis/.Cedartown, Georgia

© Prentice-Hall, Inc.

Interpreting Political Cartoons

1. What animal is the President riding? Why is this animal an appropriate choice?

2. What is President Bush's proposed solution for the economy? How do we know this?

3. What common stereotype associated with President Bush is the basis for this cartoon?

4. **Identifying Assumptions** What assumptions did the cartoonist make about the possibility that Bush's solution would help the economy?

CHAPTER 13

Section 2
Presidential Succession and the Vice Presidency

While the position of President of the United States is a powerful one, the position of Vice President remains mostly ceremonial. Still, choosing a vice presidential candidate has become a challenge because the choice can impact the campaign of the presidential candidate. Study the cartoon below and answer the questions that follow.

Dan Lynch/Fort Wayne Journal Gazette

Interpreting Political Cartoons

1. Who do the characters making the announcement represent?

2. What is the reaction of the public to that announcement?

3. What is the reason for that reaction?

4. What is the significance of the fact that the announcements of the two characters are made at the same time and are received in the same way?

5. **Demonstrating Reasoned Judgment** Explain the advantages and disadvantages of giving the Vice President more than just ceremonial responsibilities.

Section 3

Presidential Selection: The Framers' Plan

The Framers of the Constitution believed that the electoral college was a compromise between holding a popular vote and allowing Congress to decide who would be President. One of the results of that compromise has been that the popular vote and the electoral vote do not always match. For example, in 1972, Republican candidate Richard Nixon won 61 percent of the popular vote, but carried 49 States, winning 520 of 538 electoral votes, or about 97 percent of the electoral votes. Study the cartoon below and answer the following questions.

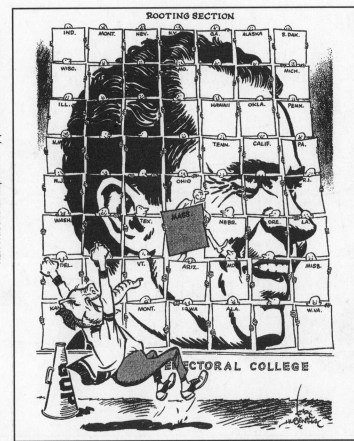

Karl Hubenthal/Reprinted by permission of E.H. Hubenthal

Interpreting Political Cartoons

1. Whose face is pictured in the cartoon?

2. What are the States shown meant to represent?

3. Which party is shown rooting for the candidate?

4. Which was the only State not carried by the winner?

5. **Expressing Problems Clearly** Would the electoral system be improved by eliminating the electoral college and relying solely on a popular vote?

Section 4
Presidential Nominations

Since 1952, New Hampshire has been the first State in the nation to hold its presidential primary. This primary has come to set the stage for the presidential nominations of both major parties, giving this small State significant influence. Study the cartoon below and answer the questions that follow.

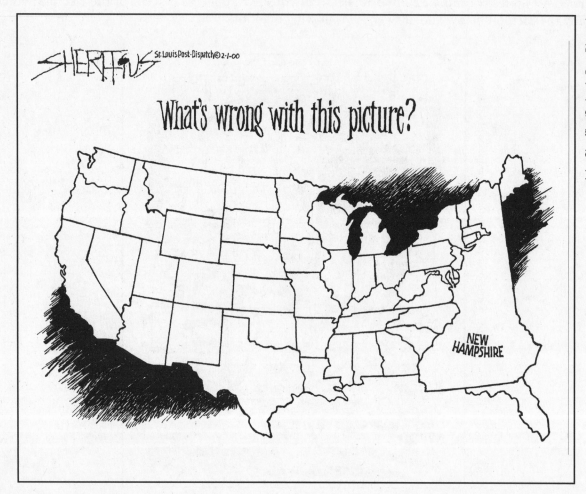

John Sherffius/St. Louis Post-Dispatch

© Prentice-Hall, Inc.

Interpreting Political Cartoons

1. What is the answer to the question asked in the caption?

2. What is the cartoonist's attitude toward the primary process?

3. Name at least three States on your map which should have more clout than New Hampshire because of their greater size.

4. **Making Comparisons** Do you favor retaining the current primary system or would you prefer to see either a national primary or a series of regional primaries as an alternative?

The cartoon below was published in November 2004, shortly after the presidential election took place. The campaign between President George W. Bush and Senator John Kerry, like many previous presidential campaigns, included both principled debates and personal attacks. The two candidates were closely matched and Bush won re-election by fewer than three percentage points. Study the cartoon below and answer the questions that follow.

Gary Markstein/Copley News Service

Interpreting Political Cartoons

1. What metaphor does the cartoonist use for the presidential campaign?

2. What does the mud symbolize?

3. Is the cartoonist positive or negative about the election process? Explain.

4. **Identifying Alternatives** How might this cartoon have looked if John Kerry had won the 2004 election? How different would it be?

CHAPTER 14

Section 1
The Growth Of Presidential Power

Andrew Jackson, President of the United States from 1829 to 1837, inspired both admiration and scorn. By some, he was loved and considered the common people's friend. By others, he was hated for wielding immense political power. Many cartoonists of his era portrayed President Jackson as "King Andrew I." Study the cartoon and answer the questions that follow.

Bettmann/CORBIS

Interpreting Political Cartoons

1. What is pictured under Jackson's right foot?

2. Jackson's critics often said Jackson "ruled with the power of the veto." Give two examples of how the cartoonist illustrates this criticism.

3. What do you think the cartoonist is trying to say about Jackson by portraying him as a king? Is this a positive or negative portrayal?

4. **Identifying Alternatives** How else might a cartoonist portray President Jackson as an overly strong leader? How might a cartoonist who supports Jackson portray the President as a leader of the common people?

© Prentice-Hall, Inc.

Section 2

The President's Executive Powers

United States Presidents have been appointing Cabinet members for over two hundred years. Although these appointments are subject to Senate approval, the President has rarely been denied the privilege of his first choice. The cartoon below addresses the process of approving Cabinet members. Study it and answer the questions that follow.

"OTHER THAN YOUR FRIENDSHIP WITH THE PRESIDENT, MR. BONZO, WHAT QUALIFIES YOU FOR THIS CABINET POSITION?"

Interpreting Political Cartoons

1. Years before Ronald Reagan became President in 1980, he starred in a film about a monkey named Bonzo, called *Bedtime for Bonzo*. How is the cartoonist relating this to the issue of appointing Cabinet members?

2. What point is the cartoonist making about the process of Senate approval?

3. Do the senators seated beside the monkey look concerned? How does this play into the message of the cartoon?

4. **Demonstrating Reasoned Judgment** The President must have the consent of Congress to appoint Cabinet members, but not to dismiss them. Do you believe this is the best policy for the country? Explain your position.

Section 3
Diplomatic and Military Powers

During the Presidency of Bill Clinton, U.S. peacekeeping troops were deployed in many locations at the same time, presenting a challenge to the President's ability to develop a comprehensive foreign policy. Study the cartoon below and answer the questions that follow.

Interpreting Political Cartoons

1. What does the large figure on the right represent? What is President Clinton saying to this figure?

2. How many arms does the figure have? Why are the figure's arms and legs twisted?

3. What does this cartoon imply about how the Clinton administration was conducting foreign policy?

4. **Drawing Conclusions** Recent Presidents have taken a strong hand in developing and implementing foreign policy. Do you think this power should be shared more with Congress? Explain your opinion.

The President is involved in the lawmaking process not only at its end, when he signs or vetoes legislation passed by Congress, but also at its beginning, when he proposes legislation. Members of Congress who are in the President's party often look to the President for bold new initiatives. Members of Congress who are in the opposing party often have a different view of presidential initiatives. Study the cartoon below and answer the questions that follow.

Interpreting Political Cartoons

1. What do the lines, "Do something...but not that!" mean?

2. Irony is saying the opposite of what one means. How is the title of this cartoon ironic?

3. Why would some members of Congress want strong action by the President?

4. Why is it unlikely that Congress will pass any bill proposed by the President without making at least some changes to it?

5. **Making Comparisons** Why is it generally easier for the President than for Congress to take a clear public stand on an issue?

CHAPTER 15

Section 1
The Federal Bureaucracy

As the United States has grown, so has the Federal Government. It is now an extensive bureaucracy that requires millions of employees to run hundreds of agencies. Study the cartoon below and answer the questions that follow.

"If made into paper it could supply the entire federal government for 16 minutes."

Ken Alexander, Courtesy San Francisco Examiner

© Prentice-Hall, Inc.

Interpreting Political Cartoons

1. What is the setting of the cartoon?

2. What is the cartoonist implying about the Federal Government?

3. Why would a large bureaucracy use a large amount of paper?

4. **Expressing Problems Clearly** What kinds of problems can result from the existence of a large, complex bureaucracy?

The Office of Management and Budget is a small but extremely influential agency of the Executive Office. Its primary responsibility is the preparation of the federal budget. David Stockman was President Ronald Reagan's first director of that office. Stockman left that post in 1985, leaving behind a huge budget deficit. Study the cartoon below and answer the questions that follow.

Interpreting Political Cartoons

1. What is the reaction to Stockman's statement in the first frame?

2. What is the reaction in the second frame?

3. Summarize the main idea of the cartoon.

4. **Predicting Consequences** What would happen if the entire government was run exactly like a business?

CHAPTER 15

Section 3
The Executive Departments

The addition of the Department of Homeland Security in 2003 raised the number of Cabinet departments to 15. The Department of Homeland Security brought together hundreds of agencies to form one of the largest departments within the Cabinet. Study the cartoon below and answer the questions that follow.

Ed Stein/ Rocky Mountain News

© Prentice-Hall, Inc.

Interpreting Political Cartoons

1. What do the objects on the floor represent?

2. What is the figure in the middle of the cartoon trying to do?

3. What statement is the cartoonist making by including such unusual items as a kitchen sink and a bowling ball?

4. **Identifying Central Issues** What do you think was the purpose of creating the Department of Homeland Security from existing agencies?

Independent Agencies

The Federal Government was shut down twice in 1995—once in November and once in December—because of budget disputes between President Bill Clinton and Republican members of Congress. An unintended consequence of the shutdown was the stimulation of thought as to just how essential some government agencies are. Study the cartoon below and answer the following questions.

Interpreting Political Cartoons

1. What real independent agency might the U.S. Clear Cutting Service represent?

2. What is the irony of the caption, "These essential federal agencies will remain operating to serve you"?

3. What question does the cartoonist raise about federal agencies?

4. **Distinguishing False from Accurate Images** Do you think many Americans see their federal agencies as they are portrayed in this cartoon?

CHAPTER 15

Section 5
The Civil Service

Recent efforts to reduce Federal Government spending have focused not just on the size of federal programs but also on the number of federal employees. The Clinton administration's National Performance Review recommended changes that would make the government run more smoothly and with fewer workers. Still, the public perception exists that the federal bureaucracy contains too many workers who do too little work. Study the cartoon below and answer the questions that follow.

Interpreting Political Cartoons

1. Who are the people in the cartoon?

2. Why are they unhappy?

3. What message is the cartoonist sending by showing the people at a coffee machine?

4. Explain the meaning behind the statements of the four employees.

5. **Distinguishing False from Accurate Images** Why do you think many Americans think that the federal bureaucracy is overstaffed and inefficient?

Complaints about high government spending are nothing new. This cartoon, dating from 1929, shows the taxpayer being drained of tax revenue to support government spending. Study the cartoon below and answer the questions that follow.

J. N. "Ding" Darling Foundation. Reprinted with permssion.

PLENTY OF WATER IF THERE WERE NO LEAKS

Costs of government had increased nearly every year during the 1920's, at the federal, state, and local level. This 1929 cartoon summed up the situation and emphasized what was being done and what should be done.

Interpreting Political Cartoons

1. What structures are shown standing on top of the taxpayer? What labels are on these structures?

2. Who are the people approaching the taxpayer? What do they plan to do?

3. Where does the "water" drawn from the taxpayer end up? Who are the consumers of this water?

4. What happens to some of the water on the way to its consumers? What does this represent?

5. **Drawing Conclusions** Summarize the cartoon's attitude toward taxation and government spending.

CHAPTER 16

Section 2
Nontax Revenues and Borrowing

Reducing the public deficit, or debt, has been a concern for many Americans. Although many agree that the debt should be paid, there is little agreement on how this should be done. Some feel that budget surpluses should be used. Others rely on the idea that the deficit will be automatically reduced if taxes are drastically cut and that money is reinvested, generating more economic activity. Study the cartoon below and answer the questions that follow.

"And on my left is 'The Great Fantino,' who takes the position that the deficit *will* disappear by magic."

Interpreting Political Cartoons

1. Who is the person on the left supposed to be?

2. What is the caption implying?

3. What is the cartoonist's position on the deficit?

4. How would Americans benefit from the deficit "disappearing by magic"?

5. **Identifying Alternatives** Suppose the man sitting to the other side of the television anchor is expressing a different opinion. What might that opinion be?

Section 3
Spending and the Budget

Ben Franklin once said "…in this world nothing is certain but death and taxes." It could also be said that as long as there are taxes, there will certainly be debates on how much taxes should be raised or lowered. How this debate is decided in our time may have a great impact on future generations. Study the cartoon below and answer the questions that follow.

Interpreting Political Cartoons

1. What relationship is the cartoonist suggesting between free tax cuts and grandchildren?

2. Explain the use of the word "free" on the machine.

3. Why might the economic strategy suggested in the cartoon seem attractive?

4. **Identifying Assumptions** What assumption does the cartoon make about how the deficit should be paid?

Section 1
Foreign Affairs and National Security

The United States, the world's only superpower, actively pursues various foreign policy goals around the world. Sometimes its goals lead to military intervention, but civilian and military leaders are usually cautious about activities that may put U.S. troops in danger. The cartoon below examines this issue. Study it and answer the questions that follow.

"World War III? Hmm. O.K., but, remember, nobody gets hurt."

Interpreting Political Cartoons

1. Who are the people shown in the cartoon?

2. Who does the Constitution say is the commander in chief of U.S. military forces?

3. What does the cartoon imply about the idea of military control of our defenses?

4. **Predicting Consequences** What do you think is the downside of an American policy which avoids having casualties under any circumstances?

Section 2

Other Foreign and Defense Agencies

The need for an intelligence gathering service to alert the American people to the threat of terrorism is vital. However, for a number of years stories in the media about problems at the CIA have undermined confidence in that institution. Study the cartoon below and answer the questions that follow.

Bruce Beattie/Daytona Beach News Journal/Copley News Service

© Prentice-Hall, Inc.

HOW THE CIA GATHERS INTELLIGENCE

① SATELLITE IS AIMED AT A TARGET

② HIGH-RESOLUTION CAMERA MAGNIFIES THE IMAGE...

706-51

TOP SECRET

NEWS
INDIA TESTS NUKES

③ VOILA.

BEATTIE

Copley News Service
©98 Daytona Beach News-Journal

Interpreting Political Cartoons

1. Describe what is happening in the cartoon.

2. What is the significance of the middle frame?

3. What does the third frame imply about the ability of the CIA to gather intelligence?

4. What do you believe is the attitude of the cartoonist toward the CIA? Explain.

5. **Making Reasoned Judgments** Do you believe that a government agency should spy on its own citizens?

Section 3
American Foreign Policy Overview

With the development of the intercontinental ballistic missile after World War II, the United States became much more vulnerable to foreign attacks. Since the 1980s, there has been a debate in Congress as to whether the government should invest in an expensive system which could shoot down incoming missiles. Study the cartoon below and answer the questions that follow.

NATIONAL MISSILE DEFENSE
(PROTOTYPE)

U.S.A.

REX BABIN THE SACRAMENTO BEE

Rex Babin/The Sacramento Bee

© Prentice-Hall, Inc.

Interpreting Political Cartoons

1. What is the setting of the cartoon?

2. What is the significance of the word "prototype" in the title?

3. What does the setting of the cartoon suggest about how the missile defense system positions the United States in the world?

4. Do you think the cartoonist is a supporter or opponent of a national missile defense? Explain your answer.

5. **Identifying Alternatives** Describe a cartoon that would express the opposite side in the debate.

Section 4

Foreign Aid and Defense Alliances

Since the collapse of communism in the former Soviet Union, the United States has become the only superpower in the world. This role as the "world's policeman" causes the United States to face many challenges. Study the cartoon below and answer the questions that follow.

"We have no friends, just allies."

Interpreting Political Cartoons

1. Who are the two figures seen in the cartoon?

2. Who do these figures represent?

3. What is the significance of the caption?

4. **Identifying Assumptions** Is it important for a country to have "friends" or is having "allies" sufficient?

Section 1
The National Judiciary

Our judicial system is a blend of federal, State, and local courts that work together. Courts at all levels have often been criticized for having too much power to interfere with family matters. Study the cartoon below and answer the following questions.

THE MODERN AMERICAN EXTENDED FAMILY

Interpreting Political Cartoons

1. What does the cartoon suggest about the relationship between the various courts shown in the cartoon?

2. What is the connection between the phrase the "Modern American Extended Family" and the court system?

3. Why do you think the family is frowning? Why are the judges smiling?

4. **Drawing Conclusions** What would happen to families and their members if the judicial system could not play any role in their lives?

The only thing "inferior" about federal district courts is that they are the courts beneath the Supreme Court. The federal district courts have original jurisdiction over most cases heard in the federal court system. Many of the decisions made in the 91 federal district courts are final; however, some cases are appealed to the higher courts. Study the cartoon and answer the questions that follow.

"*And don't go whining to some higher court.*"

Interpreting Political Cartoons

1. What has just happened to the man on the left?

2. If a judge did not allow a case to be appealed, what right would the judge be violating?

3. What is the highest court this man could appeal to?

4. **Drawing Conclusions** Summarize the cartoonist's attitude toward the judicial system and judges.

Section 3
The Supreme Court

Courts from the lowest to the highest levels have had to cope with an increasing number of cases in recent years. The Supreme Court, as the court of final appeal in the United States, receives thousands of appeals each year. It has time in each session to consider only a fraction of these. Study the cartoon below and answer the questions that follow.

Bob Schochet/1974 Saturday Review Magazine

SCHOCHET

"We might as well abolish the lower courts.
All the cases are coming to us anyway."

© Prentice-Hall, Inc.

Interpreting Political Cartoons

1. Who are the people shown in the cartoon? How do you know?

2. Explain the meaning of the justice's statement.

3. Do you think the justice's statement is meant to be taken seriously? Explain.

4. **Predicting Consequences** Why doesn't the Federal Government deal with the Supreme Court's large workload by creating a second Supreme Court to handle the extra cases?

Section 4
The Special Courts

In 1997, Senate hearings revealed a host of problems taking place within the IRS, including intimidation of taxpayers and corruption. In response, the government instituted several reforms—among them was allowing taxpayers to take the IRS to court with greater ease. Cases involving the IRS are heard by a special court, the United States Tax Court. Study the cartoon below and answer the questions that follow.

Gary Brookins/Richmond Times-Dispatch

"THE BURDEN OF PROOF ON US ?... WHAT ?!... AND LET THE TAXPAYERS THINK THEY'RE INNOCENT UNTIL PROVEN GUILTY ?!"

Interpreting Political Cartoons

1. How does the cartoonist portray the IRS?

2. What illustrations in the cartoon contribute to the image the cartoonist is conveying?

3. What does it mean for the IRS to carry the burden of proof?

4. **Distinguishing Fact from Opinion** People have historically had negative feelings toward the IRS, even before the agency suffered internal problems. Why might people have such distaste for the agency?

CHAPTER 19

Section 1
The Unalienable Rights

The 1st Amendment guarantees many individual freedoms, including freedom of speech. This particular right has long been debated and defended in this country. However, there is much less discussion and debate of the responsibilities that go along with this right. Study the cartoon below and answer the questions that follow.

Brumsic Brandon, Jr. and Florida Today

© Prentice-Hall, Inc.

Interpreting Political Cartoons

1. Who are "shock jocks"?

2. What is the figure on the left side, which is only partially seen, meant to represent?

3. What does the box labeled "responsibility" mean?

4. Where does the cartoonist seem to stand on the subject of responsibility vs. freedom of speech?

5. **Demonstrating Reasoned Judgment** Explain the advantages and disadvantages of increasing the responsibility which goes along with freedom of speech.

Section 2
Freedom of Religion

Some of the most hotly debated Supreme Court cases in recent years have involved religion. The Constitution forbids the government to establish a religion or to interfere arbitrarily with people's exercise of religion. In cases such as school prayer, however, some people have argued that government efforts to prevent establishment of religion have interfered with people's exercise of religion. Study the cartoon below and answer the questions that follow.

Gene Basset

BASSET—ATLANTA JOURNAL

Interpreting Political Cartoons

1. Describe what is happening in the top frame of the cartoon.

2. Why do you think someone in the second frame calls for a conservative Supreme Court?

3. Explain the statement in the third frame.

4. **Making Comparisons** Write one sentence that summarizes the view in support of school prayer and one sentence that summarizes the view in opposition to school prayer. Each statement must refer to the Constitution.

© Prentice-Hall, Inc.

Section 3
Freedom of Speech and Press

The Supreme Court has interpreted the First Amendment to protect desecration of the American flag. This First Amendment issue is one of many that has sparked much debate in this country. Study the cartoon below and answer the questions that follow.

Jeff Parker/Florida TODAY

Interpreting Political Cartoons

1. Who is the man wrapped in the flag supposed to represent?

2. Which part of the Bill of Rights is this man supposed to be stepping on?

3. According to your textbook, what kind of speech is being portrayed in this cartoon?

4. What is the cartoonist's attitude toward the issue presented here?

5. **Drawing Conclusions** Write one sentence summarizing each side of the debate about flag desecration and the First Amendment.

Section 4
Freedom of Assembly and Petition

Protests, rallies, and demonstrations have a long history of First Amendment protection in the United States as freedom of assembly. Today, there is much media coverage of these demonstrations. Sometimes extreme measures are used by protesters to get attention, as was the case at the meeting of the World Trade Organization in Seattle in 2000. Study the cartoon and answer the questions that follow.

Interpreting Political Cartoons

1. What is happening in the first frame?

2. How does the man in the second frame respond to the protestor?

3. Do you think the point of view of the cartoonist fairly portrays the actions of the protesters?

4. **Recognizing Cause and Effect** What impact do you think the media coverage of protests has on protest demonstrations? Do you think the media has responsibility for that impact?

Section 1
Due Process of Law

The United States system of justice is dependent upon balancing the rights of both the victims of crimes and the people who are accused of committing crimes. Over time, people's understanding of protecting the rights of the accused has evolved. Study the cartoon below and answer the questions that follow.

REGALIA THE DAILY CALIFORNIAN

JUSTICE

VICTIM

CRIMINAL

Doug Regalia/Daily Californian

"THE PENDULUM OF JUSTICE"

Interpreting Political Cartoons

1. Who do the three figures in the cartoon represent?

2. A pendulum swings back and forth without stopping. What is the importance of the swinging pendulum in the cartoon?

3. What is happening to the victim?

4. What is the relationship between the figure in the middle and the one on the right?

5. **Distinguishing False from Accurate Images** Why do you think that many people believe the scales of justice are tipped unfairly in the direction of criminals in this country?

© Prentice-Hall, Inc.

Political Cartoons

Section 2
Freedom and Security of the Person

Does the 4th Amendment's guarantee against "unreasonable searches and seizures" apply to automobiles? Though the Supreme Court has considered a number of cases on this issue, it remains controversial. Study the cartoon below and answer the questions that follow.

©Bruce Beattie/Daytona Beach Morning Journal.
Reprinted by permission of Copley News Service.

"We've looked everywhere for your constitutional protection against illegal search and seizure... but we haven't found any yet!"

By Beattie for The Daytona Beach Morning Journal

© Prentice-Hall, Inc.

Interpreting Political Cartoons

1. Describe what is happening in the cartoon.

2. Explain the policeman's statement.

3. Does the cartoonist believe that the 4th Amendment applies to automobiles? Explain.

4. What difference between vehicles and fixed residences accounts for the different way the 4th Amendment is applied to them?

5. **Demonstrating Reasoned Judgment** Do you favor police roadblocks during holidays to check for drunk drivers? Explain your view.

CHAPTER 20

Section 3
Rights of the Accused

During the infamous Lindbergh baby kidnapping trial in 1935, photographers and journalists created a circus-like atmosphere in the courtroom. This resulted in the banning of cameras in the courtroom until television coverage became widespread in the early 1990s. As a result, the media has had a greater impact on the judicial process. Study the cartoon below and answer the questions that follow.

"*Since you have already been convicted by the media,*
I imagine we can wrap this up pretty quickly."

Interpreting Political Cartoons

1. Who are the two people standing before the judge?

2. What is the American concept of law which would prevent the situation described in this cartoon from happening?

3. Which are the two provisions of the Constitution which would protect the rights of the person in the cartoon?

4. **Drawing Conclusions** Do you think that the rights of the media to cover trials impact the rights of the accused to a fair trial?

Political Cartoons

The death penalty is one of the country's most enduring controversies. Study the cartoon below and answer the questions that follow.

Stacy Curtis/The Times of Northwest Indiana

Interpreting Political Cartoons

1. Who do the two people in the cartoon represent?

2. What is the irony in the signs the two people are holding?

3. What point is the cartoonist making about the demonstrators?

4. **Identifying Central Issues** What are the major issues in considering whether the death penalty should be continued or ended in the United States?

Section 1 Diversity and Discrimination in American Society

Immigration is an important and controversial issue in many countries. What makes immigration debates in the United States especially complex is the fact that the overwhelming majority of Americans are themselves immigrants or descendants of immigrants. Study the cartoon below and answer the questions that follow.

Mike Thompson/Copley News Service

Interpreting Political Cartoons

1. Who are the people speaking in the cartoon? Who are the other people?

2. Before you saw the final frame in the cartoon, when did you think the action in the cartoon was taking place? Why?

3. Why did the cartoonist mislead readers about the setting of the cartoon?

4. **Recognizing Bias** Someone who disagrees with this cartoon might argue that the comparison it draws is unfair. Explain how this argument might be stated.

Political Cartoons

Section 2
Equality Before the Law

In 1954 the Supreme Court ruled in *Brown* v. *Board of Education of Topeka* that separate educational facilities for black and white students were "inherently unequal." Since then, despite many efforts, widespread integration of black and white students has not been completely successful. Study the cartoon below and answer the following questions.

©1972 Los Angeles Times. Reprinted by permission.

"... one nation, divisible, with liberty and justice for some."

Interpreting Political Cartoons

1. How is the top frame different from the bottom frame?

2. What are the children doing?

3. Which words in the caption have been changed from the original *Pledge of Allegiance*?

4. What statement is the cartoonist making about American society?

5. **Expressing Problems Clearly** Why do you think separate facilities, even if they look the same, were considered by the Supreme Court to be "inherently unequal"?

© Prentice-Hall, Inc.

Section 3
Federal Civil Rights Laws

Affirmative action, or the policy of actively recruiting and promoting minorities for jobs, has been criticized as reverse discrimination. Both sides of this issue are fueled by strong, often bitter feelings, as this cartoon points out. Study the cartoon below and answer the questions that follow.

Interpreting Political Cartoons

1. Who are these people and in what setting are they located?

2. What is the cartoonist trying to express by having the women reply "you tell me"?

3. Would those in favor of affirmative action consider it "preferential treatment"? Explain.

4. According to your textbook, what has been the recent trend in Supreme Court rulings in regard to affirmative action?

5. **Predicting Consequences** If the tide of public opinion and court decisions result in fewer programs of affirmative action, what would be the impact?

Section 4
American Citizenship

The borders of the United States are enormous and although immigration policies are strict, thousands of illegal immigrants are constantly attempting to enter the country. Dealing with illegal immigration and illegal immigrants has been a challenge for the government of the United States. Study the cartoon below and answer the questions that follow.

Gary Brookins/Richmond Times-Dispatch

Interpreting Political Cartoons

1. What does the lifeguard represent?

2. Who are all the people who are drowning?

3. What does the expression on the face of the lifeguard signify?

4. Would you say the cartoonist is sympathetic or unsympathetic to the plight of the illegal immigrants? Explain.

5. **Identifying Central Issues** What are some of the issues which make it difficult for Congress to deal with immigration?

Section 1
Great Britain

The essence of the monarchy today in Great Britain is that the Queen is politically neutral. She must act on the advice of the national government, which is composed of Parliament and the prime minister whose official residence at 10 Dowling Street is shown in this cartoon. As this picture humorously illustrates, in times of crisis she is probably tempted to state her views. Study the cartoon and answer the following questions.

Cookson/London Evening News

Interpreting Political Cartoons

1. Who is knocking on the door?

2. Who lives in the house she is visiting?

3. What is her mood and to what would you attribute it?

4. **Demonstrating Reasoned Judgment** Do you think the British monarchy has power over government affairs? How much power do you think the monarchy has? Explain.

The Liberal Democratic Party (LDP) dominated Japan for almost 40 years. But in 1998, voters showed they were tired of the LDP's failure to lead the country out of recession by filling 82 out of the 126 seats contested in the upper house with members of various other parties. LDP Prime Minister Ryutaro Hashimoto resigned to take responsibility for his party's poor showing. Study the cartoon and answer the following questions.

PRIME MINISTER HASHIMOTO AWAITS THE ELECTION RETURNS IN JAPAN

Interpreting Political Cartoons

1. What does the tidal wave symbolize?

2. What does the cartoonist think is going to happen to Hashimoto?

3. What power could Hashimoto have used if the seats were lost in the lower house rather than the upper house?

4. **Making Comparisons** Write a statement that summarizes the differences between the government of Japan and the government of the United States.

CHAPTER
22

Section 3
Mexico

The year 2000 marked a major turning point in Mexico. The ruling Institutional Revolutionary Party (PRI), which was in power for several decades, was pushed out when Vincente Fox, head of the National Action Party, was elected president. Fox was able to win with a message of decentralization, development, equality and—above all—change. Study the cartoon below and answer the questions that follow.

Steve Kelly/The San Diego Union-Tribune/ Copley News Service.

Interpreting Political Cartoons

1. What does the matador represent?

2. What does the fox represent?

3. Write a sentence summarizing the meaning of the cartoon.

4. **Expressing Problems Clearly** Although Fox won the election, his National Action Party does not have the majority of the seats in the General Congress. How might this affect his ability to bring about change in Mexico?

When Russia's Vladimir Putin became president in 2000, he faced the job of dealing with the social, economic, and political problems still haunting Russia after decades of Communist Party rule. Russia's economy has not adapted easily to capitalism and was on the brink of ruin throughout much of the 1990s. Study the cartoon below and answer the questions that follow.

"OK . . . We've got the Russian economy back on its feet. Now what?!"

Bruce Beattie/Daytona Beach News Journal/Copley News Service.

© Prentice-Hall, Inc.

Interpreting Political Cartoons

1. What does the coffin represent?

2. What is the cartoonist implying about the past state of the Russian economy?

3. Does the cartoonist think the economy is now in better condition or that it still needs work? Explain.

4. **Demonstrating Reasoned Judgment** The United States has been giving financial support to Russia to help keep its economy going. Do you think that best serves both the interests of the United States and Russia? Explain your position.

In recent years China has been struggling to be accepted as an equal trading partner with the other countries of the world. Because of China's huge population, other countries have been interested in developing markets there. The United States has the often conflicting goals of entering China's markets and pressuring China to improve its human rights record. Study the cartoon below and answer the following questions.

Michael Ramirez/Los Angeles Times/Copley News Service

© Prentice-Hall, Inc.

Interpreting Political Cartoons

1. What structure is pictured in the cartoon?

2. What is outside the door? What does it symbolize?

3. What is the cartoonist's attitude toward free trade and human rights?

4. **Predicting Consequences** What could happen if the U.S. develops trade with China before China remedies the human rights situation?

In a free enterprise system, the economy experiences periods of rapid growth and times of slow growth or recession. At the start of the 2000s, the United States economy endured several years with little economic growth. The economy eventually recovered and began to grow quickly in 2004. Study the cartoon below and answer the following questions.

William Filint/Arlington Morning News (Texas)

Interpreting Political Cartoons

1. What was the state of the economy when this cartoon was drawn? How do you know?

2. Why is a train a good symbol for the economy in a free enterprise system?

3. **Making Comparisons** How might this cartoon have looked if drawn at a different period in the business cycle?

Section 2
Socialism

With the rise of medical costs in this country, the concept of a national health care system has become a hotly debated issue. A national health care system is a medical system which is paid for by public money raised by taxes. Countries such as Great Britain and Canada already have such a plan in place, though there are mixed feelings about their effectiveness. Study the cartoon below and answer the questions that follow.

Jerry L. Barnett, Indianapolis News 1974

Interpreting Political Cartoons

1. Who are the figures in the cartoon supposed to represent?

2. What is the implication of the caption of the cartoon?

3. What is the attitude of the cartoonist towards a national health care system?

4. **Recognizing Ideologies** National health plans are described by some as "socialized medicine," and by others as a fair system of providing health care for all. What is your opinion? Defend your point of view.

One economic consequence of communism in the Soviet Union was that basic goods such as food and clothing were, while inexpensive, always in short supply. Since Russia's transition to free enterprise, the supply of such goods has risen tremendously. Yet prices have risen as well, because the value of the currency has fallen and because the government no longer keeps prices artificially low. Study the cartoon below and answer the questions that follow.

Interpreting Political Cartoons

1. Summarize the meaning of the top frame of the cartoon.

2. Summarize the meaning of the bottom frame of the cartoon.

3. Why might a government want to keep prices low for basic goods?

4. Explain why supplies of goods will decrease if the prices of those goods are kept low.

5. **Identifying Alternatives** Suppose you wanted to ensure that poor people could afford basic goods. How might you do this without fixing prices?

Section 1
State Constitutions

It has been said that the United States is a "land of constitutions." While there is only one federal Constitution, there are also 50 other written constitutions, one for every State in the country. Together, these documents set the stage for thousands of laws citizens are subject to and thousands of rights citizens are entitled to. Throw in local ordinances, and there are more laws and rights than one could possibly remember. Study the cartoon below and answer the following questions.

"*I love you, Sharon, and these documents will advise you of certain rights you have in accordance with federal and state law, as well as variances and privileges you retain in the City of New York.*"

Interpreting Political Cartoons

1. What is the setting of the cartoon?

2. What does the cartoonist want you to think would normally happen in this situation?

3. **Drawing Conclusions** Explain the cartoonist's attitude toward local, State, and federal law.

Section 2
State Legislatures

Hundreds of bills are considered by both federal and State legislatures every year. Among them are bills that appropriate funds for State districts. Naturally, legislators would like the legislature to pass bills that appropriate funds for special projects in their own districts. Many people are critical of this type of legislation, which is often called pork barrel legislation. A common practice by many such legislators is to attach these bills to unrelated legislation at the last minute to avoid opposition. Study the cartoon below and answer the questions that follow.

7:00 am: QUALITY CONTROL AT THE SAUSAGE FACTORY

Interpreting Political Cartoons

1. Who are the people in the cartoon supposed to be?

2. What do the sausages represent? What are they on?

3. Are the workers paying attention to the sausages that are passing by? What is the consequence of their actions?

4. **Recognizing Bias** Pork barrel legislation is often criticized. What is a possible defense of this practice?

Section 3
The Governor and State Administration

In many States, voters may recall a governor from office in the middle of the term. In 2003, Governor Gray Davis of California was recalled in a special election. At the same time, voters chose Arnold Schwarzenegger to replace him as the State's chief executive. Study the cartoon and answer the questions that follow.

Interpreting Political Cartoons

1. What does the movie theater represent?

2. Why did the cartoonist choose the movie theater as a symbol?

3. Is the cartoonist positive or negative toward Schwarzenegger's candidacy? Explain.

4. **Demonstrating Reasoned Judgment** Describe the qualities you think a governor needs to govern a State effectively.

Section 4
In the Courtroom

The job of a jury is to hear a case and make a fair, impartial judgment. Some States are moving away from the use of juries, fearing that juries may not make this type of judgment. The cartoon below satirizes one factor that could lead to a not-so-impartial jury. Study the cartoon and answer the questions that follow.

© Prentice-Hall, Inc.

Interpreting Political Cartoons

1. What does the caption imply?

2. What basic type of jury is pictured here?

3. What is the attitude of the cartoonist toward juries?

4. **Identifying Central Issues** Do you think that juries can be completely isolated from outside influences? Explain your position.

The Courts and Their Judges

As you read in this section of your textbook, the State's supreme court is the highest court in the State system. Yet these courts sometimes consider cases that raise issues of federal law, and these cases are occasionally appealed to the Supreme Court. In Massachusetts in 1996, the Supreme Judicial Court ruled that employees could not refuse to work on religious holidays, such as Christmas. Study the cartoon below and answer the questions that follow.

Dave Granlund, Metrowest Daily News

Interpreting Political Cartoons

1. Who are the people in the cartoon? Whom do they represent?

2. The State law struck down by the court had protected the jobs of workers who refuse to work on religious holidays. What do you think was the purpose of this law?

3. The court said that it was striking down the law because the law forced the State to define proper religious practice. Why might the court disapprove of such a law?

4. On what constitutional grounds might someone appeal this decision to the United States Supreme Court?

5. **Demonstrating Reasoned Judgment** If this case were appealed to the United States Supreme Court, and if you were a member of that court, how would you vote? Explain your answer.

The Lake County Commissioners in Indiana had a problem. The commissioners were required to rule on County Council ordinances within 10 days. But the commissioners' regular schedule made it impossible for them to act fast enough. Their solution was to hold special meetings to discuss the County Council ordinances, but they did not notify the public of the meetings, which was required under Indiana law. Their solution to a simple administrative problem embroiled them in a serious controversy. Study the cartoon below and answer the questions that follow.

Interpreting Political Cartoons

1. What do the tree house, signs, and secret decoder rings imply?

2. How do you think the cartoonist feels about the Lake County Commissioners' actions?

3. Why do you think people in a local community should have advance notice of local government meetings?

4. **Recognizing Cause and Effect** How do you think secret meetings affect our democratic process?

Section 2
Cities and Metropolitan Areas

Under the form of government Cincinnati has had since the 1920s, the mayor has been a member of the city council, with no executive powers. Many believe that the lack of a strong-mayor system has resulted in a city council where decision-making often breaks down under endless discussion and disagreement. Under a new proposed system, a directly elected mayor would have much greater power. For example, the mayor could veto council members' votes. The reformers hope that voters will approve their plan, resulting in a more effective city government. Study the cartoon below and answer the questions that follow.

Interpreting Political Cartoons

1. What kind of meeting is taking place in this cartoon?

2. What are they "discussing" at this meeting?

3. According to the cartoonist, what is causing the chaos?

4. **Making Comparisons** Compare and contrast the strong-mayor system and the weak-mayor system.

Section 3

Providing Important Services

In recent years, greater responsibility for funding social welfare and other programs has shifted from the Federal Government to the States. This trend has placed a strain on many State budgets. Study the cartoon below and answer the questions that follow.

©Chris Britt

Interpreting Political Cartoons

1. Summarize the message of the cartoon in a single sentence.

2. Whom does the cartoonist appear to blame for the situation?

3. List three reasons why voters might oppose paying for government services.

4. **Recognizing Cause and Effect** Explain how elected officials might help deal with the problem shown in the cartoon.

Section 4
Financing State and Local Government

Across the United States, hundreds of communities face the same dilemma—when faced with limited resources, what should the funding priorities be? Education is almost always one of the top priorities at the State and community levels, but sometimes this need is the victim of limited resources. Study the cartoon below and answer the questions that follow.

Signs Of The Times.

©A.R. Thompson/The San Diego Union-Tribune. Reprinted by permission.

Interpreting Political Cartoons

1. What structure do the warning signs pertain to?

2. Explain how the cartoonist uses the popular phrase "sign of the times" in an ironic way.

3. How do you think the cartoonist wants funding to be used?

4. **Recognizing Bias** Why might someone not want their State or community to use funding or tax revenue to rebuild schools?

Political Cartoons

Chapter 1

Section 1, p. 4

1. the caption 2. The king is on a balcony high above the land, in a position some might consider God-like. 3. The caption's tongue-in-cheek use of the word "help" shows the cartoonist's anti-royal bias. 4. A king inherits power and is believed to rule with the approval of God. A dictator seizes power, often by force.

Section 2, p. 5

1. Hitler is holding a gun to the head of a person symbolizing German minorities, forcing them to tell the world that they are being treated well. 2. As an absolute dictator, Hitler ruled the German government and the German nation itself, so he was responsible for the government's actions. 3. They might fear government violence if they refuse. 4. Answers will vary. Students may suggest that the Nazi government wanted to avoid foreign criticism of its harsh internal policies.

Section 3, p. 6

1. A group of mechanics cannot fix a customer's car because they cannot come to an agreement on how to fix it. 2. necessity of compromise 3. The mechanics could have taken a vote and used the concept of majority rule. 4. The cartoonist appears to be arguing that businesses should not be run like democracies, implying nothing gets done.

Chapter 2

Section 1, p. 7

1. milestones in the evolution of the United States legal system 2. They are supposed to represent a circus, implying that this case was a show. 3. Answers will vary. Some might say that there is now less belief in the ability of juries to be impartial. Others might say that the Simpson trial and the reaction to it is an isolated incident in our judicial history, and does not represent the true direction of the system.

Section 2, p. 8

1. The setting of the cartoon is colonial times, just before the American Revolution. 2. the man is opposed to all forms of taxation 3. The opinions expressed by the characters are more representative of current times rather than colonial times. 4. If the view that Americans should not have to pay any taxes at all had been prevalent it might have been more difficult to raise the money necessary to raise an army and start a new government.

Section 3, p. 9

1. Betsy Ross and George Washington 2. They are trying to decide which flag to use to represent the new government. 3. They are looking at so many flags because they were starting a new country which had unlimited possibilities. The choice was difficult because they had so many factors to consider. 4. The cartoon is expressing the difficulty of starting a new country. A flag is a symbol of a nation, and the cartoonist is suggesting that the nation's founders were struggling to create a new nation.

Section 4, p. 10

1. the Framers of the Constitution 2. debating the roles of Congress and the President in declaring war 3. They refer to the power recent Presidents have used to deploy troops when needed even without a formal declaration of war. 4. Only Congress can declare war.

Section 5, p. 11

1. The pillars represent States. The pillars that are standing upright represent the States that have ratified the Constitution. 2. New York 3. North Carolina and Rhode Island 4. The cartoonist was a Federalist. The cartoon compares the ratification of the Constitution to the creation of pillars on which the nation will rest; that is, as a necessary and positive event. 5. Though approval by all States was not formally necessary, it was an important sign that the entire nation was willing to support the new Constitution.

Chapter 3

Section 1, p. 12

1. The first cartoon uses the symbol of two partners dancing; the second cartoon uses the symbol of two tightrope-walkers on the same tightrope. 2. The first cartoon labels the dance "the trust tango." The second cartoon has both characters telling each other that they must support one another. 3. It shows that the President and Congress both have the capability to check the other—each is holding onto the other's tightrope. 4. In the cartoon, the two figures can only perform the dance if they do it together; the tango is not a dance for a single person. In constitutional terms, this means that the President and Congress must work together if they are to achieve their goals.

Section 2, p. 13

1. vampires 2. One coffin represents the proposed balanced budget amendment and the other represents the proposed term limits amendment. 3. Time is running out for these amendments to ever be passed. 4. Possible answer: Show the proposed amendments as perpetual sentries standing guard outside the doors of Congress.

Section 3, p. 14

1. The coach is about to lead his Air Force Academy football team in prayer. 2. the Supreme Court 3. because the Supreme Court ruled against allowing school prayer at football games 4. Both the legislative and executive branches also have the ability to change the Constitution informally. The process of informal change is thus balanced among the three branches. Each branch can check the other's power through informal change.

Chapter 4

Section 1, p. 15

1. the three branches of government 2. The people in the black robes are the Supreme Court justices and the people on the right represent older workers, women, and the disabled. 3. By giving the States more power, the Supreme Court is cutting, or tak-

Answer Key

ing away, some of the legislative powers of the Federal Government. 4. The cartoonist is supporting federalism because he is portraying the application of States rights as being harmful to certain groups of people. 5. Answers will vary. Some students might think that the States are in a better position to understand the needs of the pictured groups while others might think that the federal government can do the best job of protecting minority groups. Some might argue for a role for both States and the National Government.

Section 2, p. 16
1. The driver of the truck represents the Federal Government and the man with the briefcase represents State governments. 2. The house looks old and battered because it symbolizes an old, crumbling welfare system that needs to be remodeled. 3. The driver has a sarcastic "you wanted it—you got it attitude" and the man with the briefcase looks overwhelmed. 4. Answers will vary. Some students might think States could better run welfare programs because they are more in tune with their citizens' needs. Some students might think State-run welfare systems put recipients at a disadvantage because there are no federal regulations to ensure proper assistance.

Section 3, p. 17
1. The car is moving into a State with cleaner air. 2. The cartoon implies that States have a lot of power over their resources. 3. The cartoonist probably wants to see more cooperation between the States. The caption shows the difference between State laws and implies that if there was more cooperation, residents might get better services and resources. 4. Since States have adjacent natural resources, one could render another State's regulations less effective, as this cartoon humorously demonstrates.

Chapter 5

Section 1, p. 18
1. The Democratic and Republican parties are throwing the United States workers into a pool of water. 2. The

point being made here is that neither the Democrats nor the Republicans are sympathetic to what happens to U.S. workers when they compete in world markets. 3. Workers are being forced to either "sink or swim" without any support. 4. The cartoonist seems to be sympathetic to U.S. labor. 5. The assumption here is that U.S. labor would have a hard time adjusting to the competition of world labor markets without some assistance from government. Some students may agree, focusing on the difficulty U.S. workers have when competing with the low wages workers receive in some other countries. Others might point out that the high skill level of many American workers boosts our nation's competitiveness.

Section 2, p. 19
1. The point of this cartoon is that there is so little difference between our two major parties that people's identification with and loyalty to those parties has been greatly reduced. 2. No, because someone who could change party loyalties so easily could do so again. 3. Some students might say that it is up to the parties themselves to distinguish themselves more and educate the voters more. Others might say that the parties simply reflect voters' shifting positions on issues. 4. Party leaders could help with the problem of unity by offering their representatives better clarification regarding the major issues and stances of the party. If more representatives were aware of all facets of what a particular party stands for, better decisions could be made as to party affiliations, which would lead directly to more loyalty among the parties.

Section 3, p. 20
1. The irony of the caption is that both parties think they are helping the economy without realizing that their uncoordinated efforts are making things worse. 2. Their efforts are neutralizing each other, and if left unchecked will destroy the economy by pulling it in two opposite directions. 3. The cartoonist is pointing out that the efforts of both parties are

ineffective. 4. Answers will vary. Some people might say that it is not safe to assume that the policies of either party will help the economy. Therefore one way to look at the situation is that the fact that the two parties' economic efforts cancel each other out actually creates an environment where the economy can thrive.

Section 4, p. 21
1. the 2000 presidential election contest 2. As a third-party candidate, Nader was both running for President and challenging the control the two parties hold together over the political process. 3. The cartoonist thinks Nader is too insignificant to defeat Bush or Gore. Possible details include: the relative size of the candidates, Nader's oversized boxing trunks, Nader's untied shoes 4. The results supported the cartoonist's opinion that Nader was unrealistic in claiming he could defeat Bush or Gore.

Section 5, p. 22
1. the Republican and Democrat party establishments 2. Without the support of the party establishment they have been knocked out of the competition. 3. The party establishments are celebrating because they have defeated challenges to their power. 4. The attitude of the cartoonist is that parties' leadership have enormous power over the nominating process.

Chapter 6

Section 1, p. 23
1. "Universal registration" would mean that every person, presumably over a certain age, would have the right to register to vote. 2. Characters waiting to vote include animals, who should not have the right to vote. 3. The cartoonist is trying to make the point that there is always the danger that aggressive efforts to increase voter registration and turnout may result in voter fraud. 4. Answers will vary. Some students might say that prisoners have forfeited their right to vote through their own actions. Others might say that after people have served their time they should be able to have the right to vote again.

Section 2, p. 24

1. They are giving literacy tests to voters. 2. The period before the Civil Rights movement of the 1960s, which helped end literacy tests as a requirement for voting. 3. The irony of the caption is that the people administering the test do not understand the meaning of the word *literacy*, which is the ability to read and write. 4. Answers will vary. Some students might say that a test for basic literacy skills should not be required; while others might point out that the skills to interpret and follow events needed to make decisions about candidates require a certain degree of literacy.

Section 3, p. 25

1. to encourage women to organize to support their right to vote 2. Women were beginning on a worldwide basis to pursue their rights. 3. Men who do not "make way" for women's rights will be forced out of the way. 4. Answers will vary. Women in the United States have risen to many local, State, and national political offices. However, the election of a woman to top political office is a milestone that has not yet occurred.

Section 4, p. 26

1. candidates for office 2. that they are clones of the President, or crooks, or liars, or take PAC money, or raise taxes, or ban guns, or are part of the (Washington) Beltway crowd 3. The candidates' ads have discouraged her from voting. 4. The ads are completely negative; they offer nothing positive about the candidates and tell nothing about the candidates' views on the issues. 5. Answers will vary. Students should recognize that attempts to restrict the content of political ads would have important implications for the exercise of free speech.

Chapter 7

Section 1, p. 27

1. a candidate who has run out of money during the primaries 2. to show the high cost of campaigning 3. The nominating process is critical because it narrows a large pool of candidates to the one candidate from each of the two major parties. 4. that it is too expensive and is bankrupting people who participate 5. Answers will vary. Some will say that limiting the amount of money will reduce the impact of special interests on the candidates. Others will say that this is an unfair limitation of free speech.

Section 2, p. 28

1. a computer 2. The cartoonist wants you to think in the first frame that the traditional voting box is some high tech device. 3. Voting is interactive because people's votes have an impact on the leadership of our government. 4. The cartoonist is suggesting that the voters are fascinated by high technology and might be more interested if voting involved a computer. 5. Answers will vary. Some students might say that it could make voting more convenient. Others might point to the problems of fraudulent voting and the security and anonymity of the process.

Section 3, p. 29

1. that campaign fundraising is so corrupt and deeply rooted that it can't be changed 2. The cartoonist is saying that the average voter is not shocked or concerned to hear the electoral process is corrupt. 3. Congressional efforts to control campaign spending are pictured as too little and too late, as well as a statement of the obvious as though it were news. 4. Answers will vary. Some students might say that some aspects of the image presented, while exaggerated, do contain elements of the truth. They might say congressional efforts have not really curtailed the growing influence of special interests. Others might say that some efforts to control the problem have been made and the media has been covering the story in a more effective way than is suggested here.

Chapter 8

Section 1, p. 30

1. violence 2. Parents have to contend with the powerful influence of the mass media when trying to teach lessons to their children. 3. The media paves the way for violence by bombarding us with news, films and videos about violence and war. 4. The gun lobby has an easier job when people are surrounded by messages of guns, war, and violence. 5. Answers will vary. Some students might think that the freedoms of the press and expression allow mass media to continue showcasing a lot of violence, while others might think that decreasing the amount of violence in the media will create a safer environment for Americans.

Section 2, p. 31

1. obtaining data from people who may not want to participate in a poll 2. They own guns. 3. Students may argue that people who own guns for the purpose of defending their homes from unwanted visitors may not be interested in responding to pollsters in person. 4. The cartoonist is suggesting that polls are overly intrusive. However, students might argue that it is important to measure public opinion and that although there is always some margin of error, pollsters have found ways to control for it and make polls quite accurate.

Section 3, p. 32

1. A voter cannot find a candidate—he is hidden by television crews. 2. The comment suggests that the media is more interested in covering elections than in helping voters and candidates communicate. 3. A television executive might argue that television has made it possible for a greater percentage of voters to see and hear the candidates than ever before. 4. Students might argue that familiarity with the candidates enables reporters to cover the candidates more thoroughly and accurately. Other students might argue that reporters could become overly friendly with candidates and lose impartiality. 5. Answers will vary. Students who prefer campaign commercials might argue that commercials enable voters to hear candidates directly, without the filter of the news media. Students who prefer news stories might argue that news stories are more objective and reliable than campaign commercials.

Answer Key

Chapter 9

Section 1, p. 33
1. The figure is drawn as a giant in order to show how special interests have more power than the voters. 2. The phrase implies that the members of special interest groups know that they have more power than voters, and that the voting process is just "play." 3. The money that special interest groups contribute to campaigns enables the groups to have the power they do over the political process. 4. The cartoonist thinks that special interest groups have a lot of power in elections while voters go through the motions of voting even though their actions have much less influence. 5. Answers may vary. Some students may think that continued growth of the influence of special interest groups could erode voters' confidence in government. Others might think that special interests are balanced by the checks and balances in our governmental system and by the power of the voters.

Section 2, p. 34
1. Credit card lobbyist, a member of Congress, and an average person 2. The figures on the left are teaming up against the average person. 3. The credit card lobbyist would want Congress to make it harder to declare bankruptcy to make it harder for people to avoid paying their debts to credit card companies. 4. Answers will vary. Some students might think that the image of credit card companies and Congress is unfair. They might point out that making it tougher to declare bankruptcy strengthens our economy by forcing people to behave more responsibly. Others might think the image is fair because Congress is cooperating with the credit card industry to pass a law that makes it more difficult for the average person to get needed financial relief.

Section 3, p. 35
1. The demands of the special interests outweigh the demands of the national interest. 2. The national interest is something that benefits the nation as a whole. A special interest is some-

thing that benefits only a small part of the nation. 3. There are more organizations dedicated to narrow interests than ones dedicated to the national interest. 4. It implies that government leaders are motivated more by a desire to please special interest groups than by a concern for the national interest. 5. Answers will vary. Some students may argue that members of interest groups believe their interests are the same as the nation's interests.

Chapter 10

Section 1, p. 36
1. a member of Congress and his staff assistant 2. members of Congress; members of Congress 3. The cartoonist is implying that members of Congress are using their legislative skills for their own benefit. 4. The cartoonist is probably in favor of term limits. 5. Students might state that experience is an asset, particularly in complicated fields such as making legislation, and that few legislators are as self-interested as the one portrayed in the cartoon.

Section 2, p. 37
1. While the first frame shows the Capitol, where Congress meets, the second frame shows the people cowering behind the pillars of the building. 2. They look scared and worried. 3. the people; the irony is that although the people vote for members of the "People's House," the people in this cartoon are hiding, implying that it is not truly their House—the House does not really represent their interests. 4. Answers will vary. Some students might think representatives do a good job of representing the people. Others might think that once elected, representatives become distant from the voters they represent.

Section 3, p. 38
1. The cartoonist is making the point that many people have memorized trivial songs from old television shows but do not know the names of their elected officials. 2. He is implying that if people do not know who they are, then they are free to do whatever they want. 3. Answers should reflect stu-

dents' understanding of the Congress members' pleasure that they are able to evade accountability. 4. Answers will vary. Some students might think that the voters should know more and have numerous sources of news to keep them up-to-date. Others could point out that the representatives need to work harder to keep their constituents informed of congressional activities.

Section 4, p. 39
1. members of Congress and representatives of the President 2. work on the budget 3. The cartoonist is implying that the members of Congress—along with officials of the executive—are not very good at balancing the federal budget and are too concerned with spending as much as possible. 4. checks and balances

Chapter 11

Section 1, p. 40
1. members of Congress 2. health care, social security, and paying off the national debt 3. The cartoonist is saying that tax cuts are proposed even when the government should be spending money on far more important things. 4. Answers will vary, but may include anything mentioned in the cartoon or another use for the surplus.

Section 2, p. 41
1. members of Congress and the American public 2. He is pretending to put money into the other man's cup. 3. The cartoonist thinks that Congress is taking the taxpayers' money and pretending to give them something in return. 4. Answers will vary, but should reflect students' understanding of the historical relationship between Congress and taxpayers as well as knowledge of services taxpayers often call for.

Section 3, p. 42
1. Congress 2. It represents the large amount of money the cartoonist thinks Congress is putting into the project. 3. With the help of Congress, the military can sustain the Osprey project for a very long time. 4. It seems that the cartoonist is against the funding of the project. The money

© Prentice-Hall, Inc.

streaming out of the back of the plane signifies that the cartoonist thinks Congress is wasting a lot of money.

Section 4, p. 43
1. a wrecked car 2. The cartoonist seems to think that our country is better off without the independent counsel law, because it is represented by a junked automobile being added to a pile of trashed cars. 3. the Necessary and Proper Clause 4. Answers will vary, but should reflect students' knowledge of the branches of government.

Section 5, p. 44
1. He is about to drive off in the car labeled "foreign policy." 2. Congress is telling the President not to leave without it. In other words, Congress is reminding President Reagan that he must involve Congress in foreign policy. 3. The President's frown probably means that he prefers to conduct foreign policy without congressional interference. 4. Answers will vary, but should reflect students' understanding that each branch of the Federal Government has been given the power to check the operation of the other branches.

Chapter 12

Section 1, p. 45
1. that they are shell shocked from the battles in Congress and ineffective leaders 2. that they bear a lot of responsibility for the lack of progress 3. The cartoonist is suggesting that the leaders are pretending to do battle but in reality are accomplishing little. 4. by giving the other party a victory in the next congressional elections, which would lead to a change in leadership

Section 2, p. 46
1. The cartoonist is suggesting that the idea of senators enforcing ethical standards is a myth or wishful thinking, like Santa Claus or the Tooth Fairy. 2. One cause for investigation by the Ethics Committee would be a conflict of interest where a senator has or represents people with a financial interest in a particular piece of legislation.

3. Some students might say that senators are capable of policing themselves. Others might say that oversight by peers is just not practical, and that ethical lapses should be addressed by external groups. 4. Answers will vary. Some students might argue that there have been examples where senators have conducted investigations of their peers successfully. Others might say that investigations by outside agencies are required to provide an impartial judgment.

Section 3, p. 47
1. The implication is that the culture of the Congress has its own rules which are made for the benefit of its members. 2. that much of the legislation passed is poorly written and hard to understand 3. that the members desire to exempt themselves from legislation 4. that the members give big speeches for the American people about legislation, but when it comes to voting, they vote in their own self-interest 5. Answers will vary. One view is that term limits are harmful because they take decision-making out of the hands of the voters who should be the only ones to decide if someone stays in office or not. Another view is that career politicians become complacent and have more opportunities to develop selfish interests for promoting certain legislation.

Section 4, p. 48
1. If the groundhog (of Groundhog Day) sees its shadow, there will be six more weeks of winter. 2. The implication of this kind of coverage is that the media is easily fooled by anything they are told. 3. the senators are afraid of their own shadows and are hiding from public exposure 4. Those students who favor eliminating closed-door sessions might state that Americans have a right to know the words of their elected officials in debate. Those opposing might argue that hiding sessions from the media will encourage senators to speak freely and enable them to craft more effective legislation.

Chapter 13

Section 1, p. 49
1. a snail; the economy was moving very slowly 2. Tax cuts; he is holding a stick with a carrot labeled "tax cuts" in front of the snail's face. 3. the image of President Bush as a cowboy 4. Possible answer: he thought that tax cuts would have no effect on the economy, because he compared the response of the economy to tax cuts to the way a snail would respond to a carrot.

Section 2, p. 50
1. the Republican and Democratic parties 2. apathy 3. Since the job of the Vice President is largely symbolic, the voters show no interest. 4. The significance may be that the impact is exactly the same for both parties. 5. A disadvantage may be that the importance of the Vice President is in his role as possible successor. Therefore, the Vice President could potentially enter into a conflict with the President by taking on more power. An advantage is that the Vice President, through exercising more power, would get the chance to be better prepared to lead the country.

Section 3, p. 51
1. President Richard Nixon 2. the electoral college 3. Republican 4. Massachusetts 5. Answers will vary. Some students might say that the only true representation of the people's will is through a strictly popular vote. Others might point out that the electoral college offers a way to resolve a very close election in Congress.

Section 4, p. 52
1. New Hampshire is shown as much too large. 2. The implication of the cartoonist is that New Hampshire has become much too important in the primary contests at the expense of the rest of the country. 3. Answers will vary, but may include California, Texas, and Florida. 4. Answers will vary. Some students might defend the current system because it forces the candidates to campaign in a variety of States, debating the issues in detail. Others might

Answer Key

say that the system is too expensive and time-consuming and gives too much power to a few small States.

Section 5, p. 53
1. a boxing match 2. Personal attacks or negative campaigning; both are referred to as "mudslinging" 3. Negative; mudslinging has a bad connotation and the cartoonist implies that it dominated the election. 4. Possible answer: it would look very similar, except the referee would be holding up Kerry's hand instead of Bush's. The cartoonist holds both candidates equally responsible for the dirtiness of the campaign.

Chapter 14

Section 1, p. 54
1. the Constitution 2. Jackson is holding veto papers in his hand and the cartoonist has written "Of Veto Memory" alongside the cartoon. 3. The cartoonist portrayed Jackson as a king because this symbolizes someone who has great political authority. It is a negative portrayal because it is implying that he overstepped the power of a President, who is supposed to govern along with Congress and the opinions of the American people. 4. Answers will vary. Possible answers: Jackson controlling puppets that represent all facets of government for the negative portrayal; Jackson dressed in common clothes, leading a parade of citizens dressed in the same clothes.

Section 2, p. 55
1. The cartoonist is implying that just because Reagan knows Bonzo the monkey, Bonzo could become a Cabinet member as a result of the appointment process. 2. The cartoon is implying that Presidents can choose, and the Senate will approve, even a ridiculously unqualified candidate to be in the Cabinet. 3. The senators do not look concerned. The senators' lack of concern reflects the Senate's hesitance to deny the President his appointment requests. 4. Answers will vary. Some students might defend the importance of the President to both choose and dismiss his appointees. Others might say that if the Senate has

the right to approve appointments it should also have the right to review dismissals. Students might think that if the Senate does not exercise its power to refrain from approving, it should not have the power to dismiss.

Section 3, p. 56
1. The figure represents Uncle Sam, which represents the U.S. government. President Clinton is directing the government's foreign policy by telling the figure where to place his arms and legs. 2. 3; the figure is trying to touch too many squares at once. 3. The cartoon implies that the government was trying to deal with too many nations' problems at once. 4. Some students might think that the President is in the best position to analyze and react to foreign policy crises in the shortest time. Others might think that more congressional involvement is important because it could be a good check on possible mistakes the President could make.

Section 4, p. 57
1. Congress calls for strong action by the President but then criticizes the President's specific actions. 2. The cartoonist is arguing that Congress does not really send a clear message to the White House. 3. Members of Congress who agree with the President on important issues will want him to use the powers of the presidency to advance their common causes. 4. Some members of Congress are likely to oppose the bill and will seek to weaken or defeat it. Even members who support the goals of the bill may seek changes in order to (in their view) strengthen it. 5. Answers will vary. Students should recognize that the President does not need anyone's approval before taking a public stand on an issue. Congress, in contrast, contains hundreds of members who must come to some sort of agreement.

Chapter 15

Section 1, p. 58
1. a forested park with large trees 2. The cartoonist is implying that the Federal Government is too large. 3. Students might observe that even in

today's highly computerized offices, the need for written records and instructions results in a huge demand for paper. 4. Answers will vary. Students might suggest that such a complex organization is inefficient because of the delays one can face when working with it.

Section 2, p. 59
1. acceptance and admiration 2. shock and outrage 3. The standards for success in government are much different than those in the business world. 4. Answers will vary, but should reflect students' knowledge of how the federal bureaucracy operates. Students might answer that continuing deficits would result in a change in "management"—that is, government officials.

Section 3, p. 60
1. the different agencies that would form the Department of Homeland Security 2. He is trying to put together the new Cabinet department from all of the pieces included in the box. 3. He is saying that the Federal Government faces an impossible task because many of the agencies simply don't fit together. 4. The purpose of the Department of Homeland Security was to gather different groups together to redirect them with the single goal of protecting the United States from attack. Agencies that had competing or unrelated interests before the 9/11 attack would benefit from working together to defend the United States.

Section 4, p. 61
1. the Environmental Protection Agency 2. The satirical agencies shown in the cartoon perform tasks that are harmful to citizens. Meanwhile, the caption points out that these agencies are "essential" and here to serve the people. 3. Are some federal agencies doing the job they were intended to do? 4. Answers will vary, but should reflect students' knowledge of the trend of Americans' distrust in government.

Section 5, p. 62
1. federal employees 2. They disapprove of the plan to reduce the num-

ber of federal employees. **3.** The cartoonist is suggesting that federal employees do not work hard. **4.** The "fact" that it takes several federal employees to write and mail a single letter is meant to suggest the inefficiency of the federal bureaucracy. **5.** Answers will vary. Some students may point to specific cases of government inefficiency, or frequent attacks by politicians on wasteful government spending, or the belief that large organizations are inherently inefficient.

Chapter 16

Section 1, p. 63

1. A group of windmills are shown on top of the taxpayer. Each one has the name of a different kind of tax. **2.** The people are State and local political management. They plan to install a new windmill, symbolizing new taxation. **3.** The water ends up in a trough labeled "public treasury," where it is consumed by cattle representing public needs, improvements, necessity, and welfare. **4.** It leaks out of the pipes. The leakage represents government inefficiency. **5.** Answers will vary. Students should recognize that the cartoonist opposes government waste, as well as the attempt to impose still more taxes on overburdened taxpayers, but that the cartoonist does believe government spending can serve useful purposes such as the meeting of public needs.

Section 2, p. 64

1. a magician **2.** The caption is implying that the deficit can be eliminated without any work or sacrifice. **3.** The cartoonist seems to be think that the country must take some sort of action to reduce the public debt. **4.** The government would not have to raise taxes to pay off the debt, and any consideration of using surpluses to pay it would be dropped, leaving the surplus for other uses such as program funding. **5.** Answers will vary. Students might think that the man could suggest increasing taxes and reducing spending.

Section 3, p. 65

1. The cartoonist suggests that future generations would inherit the burden of paying for things like the deficit if tax cuts are given now. **2.** The cartoonist is using "free" ironically, since tax cuts have a cost—either in reduced government services or increased deficits. These costs are symbolized by the sign saying "insert grandchildren." **3.** It might seem attractive because it allows voters both to pursue government spending and avoid taxes. **4.** The cartoonist is assuming that the deficit should be paid with current tax revenue, or reduced spending, instead of increased deficit.

Chapter 17

Section 1, p. 66

1. a group of generals and military officers **2.** the President **3.** Military control of our defenses, without civilian oversight, is portrayed here as a risky idea. **4.** Answers will vary. One danger is that the country will be afraid to commit the military when it would be in the national interest to do so because of the fear of suffering any casualties.

Section 2, p. 67

1. The CIA is using a satellite to get a magnified image of a man reading a newspaper. **2.** The middle frame shows that the satellite is focused on the United States. **3.** The third frames shows that the CIA is getting intelligence on foreign countries by spying on people reading newspapers within the United States. **4.** The cartoonist is implying that the CIA is spending a lot of money to get information that could be easily available to them. **5.** Answers will vary. Some students might say that spying on its citizens will undermine confidence in the government's ability to protect civil liberties. Others might say that it is necessary to protect the country against domestic terrorism.

Section 3, p. 68

1. The setting shows a snow globe with artificial snow and an object shaped like the United States. **2.** The word *prototype* means that this is only an idea for a possible missile defense system. **3.** The setting makes the United States seem isolated from the rest of the world. **4.** The cartoonist seems to be an opponent of the system, implying that it is not realistic and would give Americans a false sense of security. **5.** Answers will vary. Another way to draw this would be to show a map of the United States and a shield which would deflect incoming missiles.

Section 4, p. 69

1. the Statue of Liberty and Uncle Sam **2.** the United States **3.** The caption implies that our relationships with other countries is based on the fact that the United States is a superpower and has much to offer other countries. **4.** Answers will vary. While the cartoonist seems to be implying that friendship is important in foreign relations, some students might argue that countries are not like people and require effective relationships—not friendship—in conducting foreign policy.

Chapter 18

Section 1, p. 70

1. The cartoon suggests that there is a close relationship between the various courts in the national judiciary. **2.** The courts have so much power to intervene in family affairs that it is like they are part of the family. **3.** The family is not happy with the courts' interference in their lives. The judges are smiling because they feel like they are helping families, or because they enjoy the power they are able to exercise over people's private lives. **4.** Possible answers: People could not be legally married, or nothing could be done to stop incidents of domestic abuse.

Section 2, p. 71

1. The judge has just ruled in his case. **2.** the right to due process **3.** the Supreme Court **4.** The cartoonist seems to think that too many rulings are appealed.

© Prentice-Hall, Inc.

Answer Key

Section 3, p. 72

1. They are members of the Supreme Court. This is evident from the reference to the "lower courts." 2. He is saying that so many cases are reaching the Supreme Court on appeal from lower courts that these courts might as well not exist. 3. The justice's statement is not meant to be taken seriously. First, only a small number of the total cases in the lower courts reach the Supreme Court. Also, if the lower courts were abolished, the Supreme Court's workload would be far greater. 4. Answers will vary. Courts composed of different justices would give different rulings on issues. Because the Supreme Court is the highest court in the land, any disagreements between rival Supreme Courts could create great confusion.

Section 4, p. 73

1. as frightening; evil 2. the buzzard and the skull 3. The IRS has to prove that a taxpayer has done something wrong rather than the taxpayer having to prove that he or she did not do something wrong. 4. Possible answer: Although tax revenue is used for many useful programs and projects, many people do not like to pay taxes.

Chapter 19

Section 1, p. 74

1. radio talk show hosts who tend to discuss controversial subjects 2. the United States Government 3. Responsibility here refers to care that might be exerted by people who have a wide audience and the opportunity to influence many people. 4. The cartoonist seems to come down on the side of wanting greater balance between freedom of speech and responsibility for what is said. 5. Trying to get people to balance their remarks with a sense of responsibility could result in an atmosphere more conducive to a constructive discussion of controversial issues. However, greater pressure to be more responsible in one's speech could result in less vigorous discussion of important ideas and issues.

Section 2, p. 75

1. Some supporters of school prayer are trying to push the church and the state closer together. Supreme Court justices are trying to stand between the church and the state. 2. This person is unhappy at the Court's opposition to school prayer and believes that a conservative Court will support school prayer. 3. The justice is arguing that the Supreme Court's opposition to school prayer is a conservative position, presumably because that opposition is designed to protect the constitutional guarantee against the establishment of a state religion. 4. Answers will vary. Two sample statements are: "Any law that forbids school prayer violates citizens' constitutional right to freely exercise their religion." "School prayer is unconstitutional because it constitutes the establishment of a State religion."

Section 3, p. 76

1. Congress 2. the First Amendment 3. symbolic speech 4. The cartoonist seems to feel that Congress is being hypocritical, stomping on the First Amendment to protect the flag. 5. Answers will vary. Some students might say that because the flag is such an important symbol it should not be allowed to be desecrated under any circumstances. Others might make the point that it is a desecration of the flag to suppress the free speech which it guarantees.

Section 4, p. 77

1. A protestor is demonstrating against environmental threats and forced labor. 2. The second frame puts the first into perspective by showing the irony of the fact that the shopkeeper's environment is damaged and he has suffered financial loss as a result of the actions of the demonstrator. 3. One problem is that not all the protesters did damage to property. 4. The protesters may be using more violent methods because they feel it is necessary to get the attention of the media. Opinions may differ, but the ultimate responsibility rests with the demonstrators for the consequences of their behavior.

Chapter 20

Section 1, p. 78

1. criminals, police, and crime victims 2. The pendulum represents the view of the justice system toward criminals, victims, and the police. 3. The victim who has already been hurt is suffering more from the shift in the balance of justice. 4. By ducking the policeman has evaded damage by the justice system, but he will still be hurt when the pendulum swings back. 5. Answers will vary. Some students might feel that the rights of victims have not received enough attention by the justice system. Others might say that media coverage may give an unrealistic idea about how much attention is paid to the rights of criminals.

Section 2, p. 79

1. Police are dismantling a car while the driver looks on helplessly. 2. The statement means that because the police do not regard a search of the car as an illegal search and seizure, they are free to dismantle the car. 3. The cartoonist does appear to believe that the 4th Amendment applies to automobiles because the search shown in the cartoon is exaggerated and destructive. 4. Vehicles are mobile, so officers would not have time to acquire a search warrant before the vehicle left the scene. 5. Answers will vary. Students should support their opinions.

Section 3, p. 80

1. a lawyer and a defendant 2. the presumption of innocence 3. the Fifth Amendment and the Fourteenth Amendment 4. Answers will vary. Some students might say that coverage of trials, within limits, helps to educate the public about how the legal system works. Others might say that intense public scrunity can put an unfair burden on the defense to find jurors who have not been influenced by pretrial publicity.

Section 4, p. 81

1. advocates for the death penalty and against the death penalty 2. both see themselves as protecting life 3. There are arguments to be made for both

sides of the controversy. 4. Answers will vary. Some students might say in support of the death penalty that it provides just punishment and a deterrent to murder. Others might say that the death penalty does not provide a deterrent and is often applied unfairly.

Chapter 21

Section 1, p. 82
1. The people speaking are Native Americans. The other people are Pilgrims. 2. The first three frames appear to reflect present-day concerns about immigration, not concerns from the 1600s. 3. The cartoonist is pointing out that the arguments now used against immigrants could once have been used against the ancestors of many current opponents of immigration. 4. Answers will vary. Students might point out that the United States is far more densely populated than it was in the 1600s.

Section 2, p. 83
1. In the top frame all of the students are white and in the bottom frame all of the students are black. 2. The children are reciting the *Pledge of Allegiance*. 3. "Divisible" should be "indivisible" and "for some" should be "for all." 4. The cartoonist is implying that segregated schools are not keeping to the spirit of the words in the *Pledge of Allegiance*. 5. Answers will vary. Some might say that the Supreme Court's argument was that segregation itself implies one group is inferior to another, generating a sense of inferiority that affects a group's educational opportunities.

Section 3, p. 84
1. co-workers in an office 2. The cartoonist is saying that the white co-worker already has preferential treatment because he is white. 3. Those in favor of affirmative action might say that it is not preferential treatment, but simply an attempt to remedy the effects of past discrimination. 4. Recent trends have made it more difficult for more people to benefit from affirmative action laws. 5. Answers will vary. Some students could say that a reduction in affirma-

tive action could result in a level playing field where the ability to do the job is the only criteria. Others might say that only affirmative action can overcome the legacy of past discrimination.

Section 4, p. 85
1. The lifeguard represents the United States' immigration policy. 2. illegal immigrants 3. being overwhelmed 4. The cartoonist seems to be sympathetic to the illegal immigrants because he portrays them as drowning and in need of help. 5. Answers will vary. Congress must represent the interests of many people, some of whom might also see illegal immigrants as competing for their own jobs and services. Congress has to deal with the difficult issue of which country, if any, should be favored over others in immigration policies.

Chapter 22

Section 1, p. 86
1. Queen Elizabeth II 2. the prime minister 3. She is holding a newspaper asking "Who Rules Britain?." Presumably she is angry about something the prime minister has done. 4. Answers will vary, but students should recognize that the British monarchy has some indirect influence on government affairs in that the Queen selects the prime minister.

Section 2, p. 87
1. an impending electoral defeat for the prime minister 2. He will be "wiped out," or out of the government, after the election. 3. He could have used his power to dissolve the lower house, which would lead to another election. 4. Possible answer: Japan has a parliamentary form of government and a history that has been dominated by one party, while the United States has a presidential form of government and a long history of two-party government.

Section 3, p. 88
1. The matador represent the Independent Revolutionary Party. 2. The fox represents the new president, Vincente Fox. 3. Possible answer: Vincente Fox

knocked the PRI out of the leadership of Mexico by winning the election. 4. It may be difficult for Fox to get the approval of other parties on plans and legislation he proposes in his attempt to guide Mexico in a new direction.

Section 4, p. 89
1. the Russian economy 2. that it was "dead," or extremely unhealthy 3. It still needs work. They have pulled it out of despair, but they must do more to make it thrive. 4. Answers will vary. Some might believe that it is important for the United States to maintain good relations with Russia by helping it keep its economy going. Others may believe that the U.S. is just wasting money by supporting people in the Russian government who may be either ineffective or corrupt.

Section 5, p. 90
1. the Great Wall of China 2. A trash can containing a bag of garbage labeled "human rights" is outside the door. It symbolizes China's neglect of human rights. 3. The cartoonist seems to be saying that human rights are being sacrificed in order to have free trade in China. 4. Possible answers: China will continue to violate human rights and the U.S. will be seen as supportive of it, or after China sees the benefits of trading with the U.S., the U.S. could threaten to stop trading until China honors human rights.

Chapter 23

Section 1, p. 91
1. The economy, represented by a train, was in a period of recession or slow growth. The train was struggling to reach a recovery represented by a steep hill. 2. In a free enterprise system, the economy moves forward under its own power, much like a locomotive. 3. Possible answer: the locomotive might be speeding along straight track with signs warning of danger ahead or a steep slope visible in the distance.

Section 2, p. 92
1. The man sitting down represents the United States, the doctor represents the national health plan of Great

Answer Key

Britain, and the dead patient represents what the plan has done to the country. 2. The caption suggests that the United States could be the next country to suffer from the results of a national health plan. 3. The cartoonist believes the national health plan is a terrible idea for the United States. 4. Answers will vary. Some students might say it is the only way to provide affordable health care to all. Other might say it would put limits on choice and quality of health care in this country.

Section 3, p. 93
1. The Russians wanted a change from their communist past because of long lines and shortages of goods. 2. The Russians now want a change from the free market because of very high prices. 3. The government might keep prices low for basic goods in order to ensure that poor citizens can afford these goods. 4. If prices are kept low, there is little incentive to produce those goods; supplies will therefore decrease. 5. The government could, as in the United States, give poor people cash or vouchers (food stamps) to enable them to buy basic goods.

Chapter 24

Section 1, p. 94
1. a fancy restaurant in New York City 2. The couple would have a romantic dinner and the man would propose to the woman. 3. The cartoonist is poking fun both at the tremendous number of laws and jurisdictions in the country, and the tendency of some people to adapt an excessively legalistic approach toward personal matters.

Section 2, p. 95
1. legislators 2. bills in the legislature; a conveyor belt 3. No. The sausages (bills) are passed without careful scrutiny leading to a lack of "quality control." 4. Possible answer: Pork barrel legislation leads to some good projects for the local districts and gives the legislators a way to negotiate with other legislators to keep the legislative process from breaking down.

Section 3, p. 96
1. California 2. Arnold Schwarzenegger was best-known for his career in films before running for governor. 3. Positive; there is nothing negative about Schwartzenegger in the cartoon, and he is depicted as popular among the voters because he has drawn a large and diverse crowd to support him. 4. Answers will vary, but should reflect familiarity with the section.

Section 4, p. 97
1. The verdict was influenced by people outside of the jury room. 2. a petit jury 3. The cartoonist seems to think that some juries cannot properly perform their duties, as juries are not supposed to discuss a case outside the courtroom. 4. Answers will vary. Some students might think that it is impossible to keep jurors away from influences such as the media. Others might think that by physically isolating the jurors, one can isolate them form outside influences.

Section 5, p. 98
1. Santa represents the Supreme Judicial Court; his elves represent workers. 2. This law was designed to protect people's right to freely exercise their religion. 3. For the government to be in the position of defining proper religious practice could well violate the separation of church and state. 4. A person could claim that the ruling, by forcing him or her to work on a religious holiday, prevented him or her from freely exercising his or her religion. 5. Answers will vary. Students should balance the need to protect citizens' right to free expression of religion with the need to avoid establishment of an official religion.

Chapter 25

Section 1, p. 99
1. They imply that the meeting is secret and the public should not come. 2. The cartoonist appears to disagree with their actions. 3. Answers will vary, but students might think that people need to know about the meeting so they can attend if they want to have an impact on the issues discussed at the meeting. 4. Secret meetings can

undermine the democratic process by denying people the chance to be aware of, participate in, and influence the decision-making process. Students may note, however, that some public bodies, such as some congressional committees, hold closed sessions.

Section 2, p. 100
1. a city council meeting 2. They are discussing the mayoral reform plan. 3. lack of a strong mayor 4. In a strong-mayor system, the mayor is the head of city government and often has the power to make the budget, hire employees, and exercise strong leadership. In the weak-mayor system, the mayor shares most executive duties with other members of the government.

Section 3, p. 101
1. Possible answer: Voters want government projects and services but do not want to pay for them. 2. The cartoonist appears to blame voters who refuse to pay for the services they demand. 3. They might not approve of some of the services; they might feel that their part of the tax burden is unfairly high; they might suspect that government inefficiency or corruption is inflating the cost of government. 4. Elected officials could help deal with the problem by making it clear to voters that if they demand costly government services, they will have to pay for these services in the form of taxes.

Section 4, p. 102
1. the school 2. He uses the phrase to refer to the signs suggesting the poor condition of the school. 3. The cartoonist would like the funding to be used on improving school buildings. 4. Possible answer: People may not have children attending school and may not attend school themselves. They might think the money would be better spent on something that would more directly benefit them.